THE ECONOMIC
CONSEQUENCES
OF AUTOMATION

Within, let all fit implements abound,
Lest with refused intreaty wandering round
Thy wants still press, the season glide away,
And thou with scanted labour mourn the day.

Hesiod, *Works and Days*, II:31
(Transl. C. A. Elton)

THE ECONOMIC
CONSEQUENCES
OF AUTOMATION

By PAUL EINZIG

W · W · NORTON & COMPANY · INC · *New York*

CONTENTS

5

6 CONTENTS

PREFACE

AUTOMATION is a new subject, and its economic aspects have not received the attention they deserve. A small number of books, dealing mainly with its technological, social, or commercial aspects, have examined briefly also some of its economic aspects. Occasional articles by economists, and their contributions to proceedings of various conferences or inquiries, contain much interesting and valuable material. The range of economic problems they cover is, however, limited. No attempt has been made to cover systematically the wide range of the highly involved problems arising from the impact of automation on national economy and world economy.

Yet it is of the utmost importance that the general public should be enabled to take an intelligent interest in automation, not only in its fascinating technological aspects but also in its vital economic aspects. For the economic consequences of automation are liable to affect the life of every man, woman and child. And whether the change they will bring about will be for better or for worse will depend largely on the extent to which the economic aspects of automation are understood by politicians, administrators, businessmen, trade union officials, and—last but by no means least—by the millions of industrial workers.

To investigate the subject, with its manifold implications, is among the most important tasks economists have ever had to handle. It is certainly the most difficult task I have ever undertaken. To write on largely unexplored subjects is always risky because there is not much opportunity to learn from other people's mistakes. Moreover there is relatively little factual material available for analyzing its economic aspects. For, although the origins of automation can be traced back to the distant past, it is only since the end of World War II that its progress has become sufficiently accelerated to give rise to economic problems. Indeed, most economists, in so far as they have taken notice of automation at all, hold the view that it presents no problems which are not covered already by the existing body of economic principles.

One of the objects of this book is to show that this attitude is unjustified. It is my contention that automation has given rise, or is likely to give rise, to a number of special problems which call for careful analysis by economists. There are, for instance, the fundamental differences between the economic effects of automation in an expanding and a contracting economy; the circumstances in which automation is likely to create nontechnological unemployment; the consequences of the inadequate response of the output of automated industry to a decline in demand; the effects of automation on the trend of prices, on capital requirements, on business cycles, on the balance of payments, on the economic aspects of national defense, etc. In dealing with these subjects, I shall endeavor to prove that there is, or ought to be, such a thing as Automation Economics.

The main conclusion that emerges from this attempt to examine the various economic angles of the subject is that *it is of vital importance, not only from the point of view of our prosperity, but even for our survival as free nations, to proceed with automation with the utmost speed.* I do not attempt to minimize the risks and disadvantages attached to a sudden adoption of automatic methods of production by a wide range of industries. But the risks and disadvantages arising from lagging behind other industrial countries—especially the U.S.S.R.—in respect to automation are incomparably greater. Moreover the advantages of cutting down the time of the production process and the cost of production, and of expanding the output under full employment, are so immense that they make it well worth our while to take some calculated risk.

For the sake of the welfare of mankind, we must take full advantage of the amazing progress made in recent years by scientists and technologists, and encourage and facilitate further progress. To that end it is of the utmost importance that automation should not be hindered by a selfish or shortsighted attitude on the part of either side of industry. The progress of automation has, in any case, many technological, commercial, and economic limitations. It would be unpardonable to impose on it additional handicaps because of the failure of those directly concerned to realize the paramount importance of allowing it to progress unhindered.

My other main conclusion is that it has now become more important than ever to avoid a slump. Although progress of automation itself need not cause a slump, should one develop for other reasons its adverse effects are liable to be exaggerated considerably by the drastic reductions of employment and of prices that have been, or will be, made possible by automation. In order to minimize this risk, we must do our utmost to check the inflationary trend that has prevailed most of the time since World War II. The further it is allowed to proceed the more drastic will have to be the official action, which the governments are bound to take sooner or later, to prevent inflation from getting out of control. And the more drastic the disinflationary action that is taken against inflation, the graver is the risk of sliding into a deflationary spiral.

The only way of safeguarding ourselves against such a danger would be by exercising a high degree of self-restraint. This applies equally to employers, employees, consumers, and the government. All faults are seldom on one side only. But at the time of writing they are largely on the side of organized industrial labor. The wage spiral that has been proceeding in Britain and even in the United States and other industrial countries, at a rate that bears no relation to the postwar increase of productivity, constitutes a major handicap to automation. Its inflationary effects necessitate disinflationary measures from time to time, and such measures inevitably slow down the progress of automation. They also carry the possibility of a deflationary slump, with all its adverse consequences exaggerated by the effects of automation.

A careful study of the economic aspects of automation should make unions realize the imperative need for helping automation instead of hindering it. There must be, of course, every sympathy with their anxiety to avoid technological unemployment through automation, or to mitigate the hardships that such unemployment is liable to cause. But there can be no sympathy for their endeavor to create or perpetuate overfull employment for the sake of maintaining, and possibly increasing, the benefits derived from the scarcity value of labor. It is not enough to pay lip service to favoring automation while at the same time effectively hindering its progress, and increasing the risk attached to it, by accentuating the inflationary trend. Yet this is what the labor unions are doing.

On the other hand, human nature being what it is, it is perhaps too much to expect workers and their unions not to misuse their strong bargaining position so long as spectacular increases of profits and dividends result from automation. To some degree the additional risk involved in investing in automatic equipment which is liable to become obsolete in a short time justifies additional profits and dividends. But in the interests of good industrial relations, as well as of checking the wage spiral, industrial firms would be well advised to practice self-denial by lowering their prices. In addition, there is a strong case for a general adoption of the formula embodied in the Guaranteed Annual Wages Agreements, first concluded in the United States motor industry in 1955, under which a part of the profits is set aside in special trust funds, to be used for the payment of compensation to unemployed workers during periods of business depression.

There is a very great deal at stake. The need for mutual understanding to remove all obstacles that hold up automation, and to reduce the risk attached to its accelerated progress, must be appreciated by all. Realization of the economic implications of automation would be the first step towards achieving such understanding.

The first three chapters, and parts of the summary in Chapters 22 and 23, deal with technological and commercial aspects of automation, in so far as they have a bearing on its economic aspects. Chapters 6, 7, 17, and 19 are mainly concerned with its social aspects. The rest of the book examines the economic consequences of automation. Separate chapters are devoted to each of its more important economic aspects. I have chosen this method of treatment, because readers without much previous knowledge of economics may find it easier to follow the argument if each chapter is practically a self-contained essay on its respective subject. Admittedly, this involves a certain amount of overlapping, for which I feel I owe an apology to economists who may find such repetitions unnecessary.

I am greatly indebted to the authors and editors of the writings on automation listed in the first part of the Bibliography, for the information and inspiration derived from their contributions to the subject. My analysis and my conclusions are based almost entirely on the factual material they provided, covering British and American experience in automation. The second part of the Bibliography lists the works which I have consulted from the point of view of the economic background against which automation operates.

P. E.

THE ECONOMIC
CONSEQUENCES
OF AUTOMATION

CHAPTER ONE

WHAT IS AUTOMATION?

ALTHOUGH we have come across the term "automation" more and more often in everyday use during the last few years, the man in the street has only the haziest notions about its meaning. Considering the highly technical character of the subject, this is not surprising. Moreover the experts have put forward many differing definitions of the term, which does not make things easier for the layman. He is confused and mystified, and is inclined to suspect something highly involved and altogether beyond him. Yet, although the understanding of the various technical processes covered by the term certainly requires specialized knowledge, the meaning of the term itself should be easily intelligible to the general public. As our lives are liable to be greatly affected by automation, it is important that the public should take an intelligent interest in the broad non-technical problems involved, instead of being deterred from interesting itself by assuming that, like nuclear physics, relativity, the deciphering of the Dead Sea scrolls, or higher Mathematical Economics, they must be left to the expert.

Everybody knows what "automatic" means. The Oxford Dictionary defines it as "self-acting," or "working of itself." Most of us have had experience with automatic telephone exchanges, automatic lifts, and many other automatic instruments in everyday use. An increase of the extent to which

machines are functioning of themselves, without the co-
operation of human muscle or human brain, may be described
as "automatization." During the late forties this term was
streamlined by two leading American experts, Mr. John
Diebold and Mr. D. S. Harder, into "automation."

Some experts employ the term in a narrow sense, limited
by the particular automatic process in which they are
primarily interested. Thus in the electronics industry automation is regarded as synonymous with the adoption of
electronic devices. Mr. Harder, being concerned with the
automation of the Ford works through the replacement of
the assembly belt by transfer machines moving the work
pieces automatically from one press to another, defines automation as "the automatic handling of parts between progressive production processes." A broader definition put
forward by Lord Halsbury includes under automation transfer machines, electronic control of the process, and the
mechanical assembly of the components. Definitions with
an even wider scope cover not only industry but also the
adoption of automatic devices in wholesale and retail trade,
in transport and communications, in agriculture, in offices
of every kind, and even in households.

Fortunately for the writer of this book, and for the majority
of his readers, there is no need, from the point of view with
which we are here concerned, to choose between the multitude of existing definitions, or to produce an original definition, in order to determine the scope of the subject too
rigidly. Such a definition, or an enumeration and description
of the whole wide range of processes that come under it,
would be irrelevant from an economic point of view. What
matters for us is that automation, whether in the broadest
or narrowest sense of the term, is a technological method

that tends to reduce current production costs in terms of man-hours per unit of output. It has other advantages. But from the point of view of the economic problems with which we are primarily concerned—problems of employment, business trends, price trends, profits and wages, saving and investment, etc.—the difference between including within the scope of automation a narrower or wider range of automatic processes is largely one of degree. Indeed, from an economic point of view there is everything to be said for the broadest possible interpretation of the term. Its loose use practically as a synonym for advanced mechanization may shock the technologist, but serves the purposes of the economist. From a technological point of view the adoption of electric screw-drivers, for instance, is not automation, because, though power-driven, they are used by human hands. But the economic effects of the saving of man-hours through their adoption is substantially the same as if the power-driven screwdrivers were machine-handled.

Replacement of human or animal effort by machine has always been considered a goal worth pursuing. During the Middle Ages many scientists and charlatan experimenters had tried hard to devise perpetual motion to that end. In a way this idea was even more ambitious than automation, because it was to provide its own driving power, while designers of automatic devices are content to rely on electric power supply. Automation, as applied in factories, aims at achieving uninterrupted motion unaided by human effort, which transforms materials through a series of processes into the desired shape and possessing the desired qualities, transfers them to where they are required, and assembles the pieces into the final product. It aims at automatic control of the quantity, shape, and quality of the product, with the aid of self-correcting devices which inspect the goods to check whether they are in conformity with specifications, eliminate defective goods, and automatically adjust the process, if necessary, to bring the result into conformity with specifications.

As applied to offices, automation aims at entrusting machines with the execution of routine clerical work: keeping the management supplied with up-to-date information about the progress of production, sales, inventories, accounts, etc.; storing routine information in such a way as to make it available automatically whenever required and in the form in which it is required; and assisting the management to work out speedily alternative plans of action. Much of this kind of work has been done for some time past with the aid of mechanical "punch-card" systems which are now being replaced by electronic computers. Electronic devices enable managements to exercise distant control over the process of production, with the aid of instructions written on magnetic tapes which automatically ensure the execution of instructions without the intervention of human agency.

As applied to commerce, automation helps in sorting out the goods in wholesale or retail trade, and in conveying them to the desired destination. As applied to transport, automation provides for the automatic control of traffic by a system of self-regulating signals and warnings, automatic systems of booking reservations, etc. In communications, automatic telephone exchanges connect the numbers without the aid of switchboard operators.

The above description does not aim at more than indicating the broadest outlines of a system which has many other applications besides those given here. There is an extensive literature on the technological aspects of automation—some books, many more articles, reprints of addresses, published proceedings of conferences and official inquiries, which are intelligible to the layman. Most of the items included in the Bibliography belong to that category; otherwise they would have been, quite candidly, unintelligible to the present writer. They provide ample material for further reading for those who are interested in the technological problems involved. The history of the development of automatic devices, too, as well as their present-day application, makes fascinating reading. The interested layman will find that the description of many devices actually in force puts recent science fiction to shame.

It is outside the scope of this book to describe or classify the innumerable devices which are in use. But it might assist readers unfamiliar with the subject if, in addition to the above general description of the scope of automation, we were to give some characteristic instances.

In an address to the conference of the British Institute of Management in November 1955, Mr. J. L. Putman, one of the heads of the Isotope Division, Atomic Energy Authority, Harwell, explained the way in which the degree of penetration of radiation through materials is used for gauging automatically the thickness of a wide range of sheet materials, such as paper, plastic foils and rolled metal sheets. A radioactive substance is mounted at one side of the sheet of material and a radiation detector on the other side. The response of the detector to the radiation through the material indicates the thickness of the material to be gauged. This response is automatically compared with the response to a similar test of a material of the required thickness, and any deviations from the standard are indicated. If the rays that penetrate through the material are too strong or too weak, they operate switches of mechanisms that automatically adjust the production process so as to produce the required thickness. The system can be employed for gauging thicknesses varying from that of cigarette paper to steel sheets of up to four inches thick.

Automatic transfer machines secure a continuous flow of the processes of production without intervention of human labor. Instead of having to shift the work piece from one press or machine tool to another, this is done by the transfer machine which moves it from one stage to the next. The machine places the piece in precise position, fixes it there, performs the necessary operation, releases the piece, moves it to the next position, and receives the next piece. At one end the material is loaded into the machine in the form of a continuous strip; after being automatically subjected to a large number of operations, it emerges from the press as a finished part, ready for assembly. In some instances even the assembly of parts is performed automatically, though at the time of writing this is still the exception rather than the rule.

In a Cleveland automobile plant, machines perform 530 operations on an engine block as it is shifted along by other machines. The finished block emerges without having been touched by human hands. In another plant two refrigerators a minute are being turned out by a combination of 2,613 machines and tools and 27 miles of conveyors. Apart from checking the sheet metal for the refrigerators at the beginning of the process, machines do everything.

Dr. B. V. Bowden, Principal of the Manchester College of Technology in England, describes the operation of an inventory control machine, installed by a Chicago mail-order firm, dealing in 8,000 different articles. It gives a report on the stock position every day. It is worked by ten operators instead of 150 clerks who did the same work, much less satisfactorily, until the installation of the computer.

In his evidence before the Congressional Subcommittee on Economic Stabilization Mr. Walter P. Reuther, President of the Congress of Industrial Organizations, quoted a selection of remarkable instances of automatic production. He described an automatic lathe which gauges each part as it is produced, and automatically resets the cutting tools to compensate for tool wear. In addition, when the cutting tools have been worn down to a certain predetermined limit, the machine automatically replaces them with sharp tools. The parts are automatically loaded into the machine and are automatically unloaded as they are finished. These lathes can be operated for five to eight hours without attention, except for an occasional check to make sure that parts are being delivered to the loading mechanism.

A complete automatic plant is now producing mixed and ready-to-use concrete for a Cleveland builders' supply firm. Operated from an electronic control panel, the plant can produce and load into ready-mix trucks any one of some 1,500 different mixing formulae that may be demanded. This plant uses no manual labor at any point in the process. By a combination of teletype and radio, the control operator is informed as to the particular formula to be loaded into each truck as it arrives. He gets out a punched card, coded for that formula, and the automatic mechanisms take over. Specified amounts of the required materials are delivered by conveyors in precisely the right quantities to a mixing bin where they are automatically mixed and then loaded into the waiting truck.

In 1914 the Cincinnati Milling Machine Co. would have

used 162 machines, representing an investment of $234,000, to machine 108 cylinder heads per hour at a direct labor cost of 40 cents per piece. By 1949 it took 6 machines, representing an investment of $240,000, to turn out the same volume of production at a direct labor cost of 20 cents per piece. The saving is much greater than indicated by these figures, when the increase in wage rates between 1914 and 1949 is taken into account. By 1954, however, those six machines had been replaced by a single automatic machine, representing an investment of only $230,000 for the same volume of production, and direct labor costs had been cut from 20 cents a piece to 4 cents a piece—a reduction of 80 per cent in five years.

A precision-boring machine used in aircraft equipment production can bore holes with an accuracy of one thousandth of an inch. Electronic signals from a tape move the blank metal back or forward, rotate it into position, and then turn on the boring mechanism to cut the hole exactly where it is desired. The machine is especially suited for medium-sized production in lots of several hundred parts.

In Britain the Boulton and Paul works at Norwich have a gigantic automatic machine for the production of steel frames for building construction. The parts are automatically cut to the required shape and size, and holes are bored in them where needed. The work is performed more speedily and more accurately than by hand-operated machines, and much time and labor is saved thanks to avoiding mistakes arising from imperfections of human faculties.

Similar instances are quoted in the daily press almost every day; they are described in greater detail in trade papers or in the technical press. Our selection of a few examples should suffice to give some idea of the kinds of devices the adoption of which comes under the definition of automation. Most readers are, no doubt, familiar with many instances of the popular "electronic brains" operated in large offices, so that no specific description is called for.

We trust that the factual material given above has enabled the lay reader to form his own vague definition of the technological sphere covered by the term "automation." But the latest definition put forward by Diebold, that pioneer of the scientific study of automation, covers a much broader field. It seeks to go beyond the technicalities and to ascertain the spirit behind them. In the course of his address at the Conference of the British Institute of Management in November 1955, he remarked that automation implied a complete change of attitude towards production, something more than mere mechanization. It constituted a reversal of the age-old trend towards division of labor—at any rate as far as labor of machinery is concerned. Before automation, manufacturing processes were "departmentalized," to allow for the most efficient use of human skill. The limitations of the operator's potential skill determined the design of the machines and the entire production process. "With the introduction of the new concept and technology of self-regulating systems, however," Mr. Diebold went on, "it is no longer necessary to design the production process around the limitations of human skills. . . . Automation requires us to view the production processes as an integrated system and not as a series of individual steps divided according to the most economic distribution of human skills—or even of individual machines."

Mr. Diebold believes that automation is an attitude—a philosophy of production rather than a particular technology of electronic devices. The whole problem of production is approached anew—even the product itself is reappraised in terms of its function and the functions of the machines that handle it. In his standard work on the subject, *Automation— The Advent of the Automatic Factory,* he states that redesign of the product, of the process, and of the machinery is often necessary to take full advantage of the new technology. For the sake of the advantages of automation, it is worth while to adapt all three to the requirements of automatic process. A product may be in itself satisfactory. But if it cannot be produced by transfer machines, it may be worth while to change its shape or quality to make it more suitable. Or it may be worth while to produce it by a totally different process, or at any rate, with the aid of totally different machinery. In particular, in order to exchange the disadvantages of production in batches for the advantages of the continuous flow— such as exists in oil refining and in the chemical industry— it may be well worth while to re-think the whole procedure. At the beginning of this century, oil was produced by means of a batch process, but the adoption of the oil-cracking plant made continuous-flow production possible. Thanks to the automatic transfer of the product from one process to the next, the number of operatives in oil refineries has been materially reduced, in spite of the expansion of the output.

In offices too, automation means a great deal more than the installation of digital computers for the purpose of carrying out mechanically the routine work hitherto done by human agency. The entire work has to be reorganized. The operations have to be reduced to their elements, so as to become suitable for execution by the machine. Any superficial complications have to be eliminated before the machine can be put in full charge. Diebold points out that, as a first step towards automation, both office and factory have to do some hard thinking to decide whether methods hitherto pursued and taken for granted are really necessary in their existing forms or whether a drastic readjustment could secure any advantages from the point of view of their automatic performance. But for the attempt to meet the special requirements of the projected automation, the idea of uprooting some well-established routine might never have occurred to the management. In many instances such re-thinking of the system made for greatly increased efficiency, apart altogether from the additional advantages gained from automation.

Such reorganization of methods in factory and office thus constitutes an integral part of automation, even if in itself it does not constitute a technological change in the sense of increasing the automatic character of the process. On the basis of a narrower definition, the results, to the extent to which they are achieved by the reorganization, are not brought about by technological means. But from an economic point of view it would serve no useful purpose to draw such a distinction. We may safely leave it to physical scientists and technological experts to argue it out among themselves. What we are concerned with, from an economic point of view, is the effects of any major changes in employment, in cost of production, in output, in prices, wages, and profits, etc., that are liable to result from the progress of automation in the broadest sense of the term; its indirect effects on money, trade, taxation, and on the national economy and world economy in general; and its social, military, and political effects. From this point of view no precise definition is called for. It is sufficient if the reader knows roughly what it is all about.

Before concluding this introductory chapter, it is necessary for us to discriminate between the two different senses in which the term "automation" is used, irrespective of its definition. It may mean the process of adopting automatic methods of production. Or it may mean the operation of the automated industry, after the completion of its conversion to automatic production. There can, of course, be no question of ever achieving a state of complete automation, and it is likely to take a very long time before everything that can be automated will be automated to the utmost limit of technological possibility. So automation must involve, at any rate in the lifetime of the present generation, progress towards the conversion of an increasing number of firms in an increasing number of industries to an increasing degree of automatic operation. While the process may have already reached its limits in some industries, it has a fair scope for progress in most industries. When we talk about the effects of automation, we may mean either the effects of its progress as it is proceeding, or the effects after its accomplishment in so far as it has already been accomplished. Usually the context makes it clear in which sense the term is employed.

CHAPTER TWO

TECHNOLOGICAL PROGRESS

PROGRESS towards a higher standard of living can be achieved in four ways: harder work, more efficiently organized work, better exploitation of natural resources, and improved technological methods. In this book we are only concerned with the last-mentioned way of raising the standard of living. Thanks to the invention of new technological devices and their practical application it is possible to increase the output of goods and services per head of the population even if the population works less hard. Automation does, of course, imply more efficient organization of labor, and the resulting increase in the output does imply the tapping of additional natural resources. What we are concerned with in this chapter is the circumstances leading to technological progress.

Such progress is achieved in three stages. First, there must be progress in science—that is, in the elaboration of theoretical foundations for technological innovations. It is, of course, possible for inventors with no scientific training to stumble on brilliant ideas, or to produce some invention by purely practical experimenting through trial and error. In particular, men in factories often discover important improvements to their machines, without any theoretical background. Generally speaking, however, technological progress has for its foundation a previous progress of science; or, at any rate, practical results are consolidated, and their scope enlarged, through the subsequent creation of theoretical foundations for them.

The second stage is the technological application of scientific progress by means of inventions. This is usually accomplished by a different set of people, with essentially practical training. It is, of course, an advantage to inventors to be well versed in science, at any rate to a sufficient extent to enable them to appreciate and apply the scientific principles elaborated by theoretical experts. In particular a knowledge of advanced mathematics is very helpful.

Finally, there is the stage of commercial utilization of technological inventions. Inventors have to convince somebody, either an industrial firm or a government department, of the practical possibilities of their inventions. The firms or government departments in turn have to be able to secure the necessary financial resources for the exploitation of the invention. They also have to secure the necessary physical means of production and distribution. And, last but by no means least, there must be an adequate effective demand for the goods produced with the aid of the inventions.

The conflict between the "great men" interpretation of history and its determinist interpretation exists also in the sphere of the history of technological progress. One school of thought believes that such progress depends on the accident of the appearance on the scene of prominent scientists and inventors, and of people able to grasp the practical significance of their inventions. According to this theory, the pace of technological progress depends on purely fortuitous circumstances—whether or not men of genius happen to live in a particular period.

The opposite school believes that great scientists, inventors, and utilizers of inventions, are created largely by circumstances determined by the pressure of urgent and imperative requirements, and by the resulting development of those conditions in which research and the application of its results are financed liberally. Circumstances which, according to this school, may lead to an acceleration of the pace of technological progress include war or arms race, economic isolation or race for economic supremacy, overpopulation or labor scarcity, shortage or excess of raw materials, etc. They are all liable to create situations in which the government and private enterprise are inclined to encourage research. But apart from any such circumstances, their attitude may be affected through some change in the fashion of thinking. The educational system may also take the initiative by deciding to divert more attention to technological education.

Institutional changes in the financial system or in monetary policy may also play a decisive part, by determining whether money should be plentiful or scarce for the requirements of research and the utilization of innovations. Economic trends may be of decisive importance. Booms are bound to encourage technological progress while depressions are liable to discourage it, even though declining demand and prices provide inducement to cut down costs with the aid of labor-saving innovations. Finally, changes in social policy, leading to a redistribution of incomes, are also liable to affect technological progress through influencing the nature and extent of consumer demand, or through influencing the amount of capital available for investment in the latest equipment.

The acceleration of technological progress since the war has been the result of the combination of an unusually large number of circumstances. To some extent it had its origins in wartime conditions. National self-preservation provided the maximum inducement to concentrate the utmost effort on inventions and their exploitation, in order to meet the needs of national defense. Automation was greatly stimulated by wartime scarcity of labor. Since a large proportion of the nation's manpower and womanpower was serving in the fighting forces, it was essential to replace them by machines as far as possible. Automation was hindered, however, by the need for keeping down capital expenditure. It was largely confined to top-priority new plants or plant extension directly connected with vital arms production or economic war effort.

A much more important contribution of the war to the progress of automation was the co-ordination and integration of various branches of scientific and technological research under the auspices of the government, with virtually unlimited financial and material resources placed at their disposal. Some of the innovations invented or developed during World War II—such as radar, automatic gunfire control, guided missiles, etc.—involved principles which became extremely useful in postwar scientific and technological research for civil purposes. There can be no doubt that the war greatly hastened the development of electronics, which came to play such an important part in the postwar progress of automation.

The following are the most important postwar factors that have contributed towards the progress of automation:

(1) Postwar scarcity of labor,
(2) Rising trend of real wages,
(3) Expansionary monetary policy,
(4) Increased consumption through inflated purchasing power,

(5) The stimulus of rising prices,

(6) The increased use of instalment credits,

(7) Active government intervention in the sphere of research,

(8) Progressive realization by industry of the importance of research,

(9) Pressure of circumstances arising from the "cold war."

The wartime shortage of labor continued to a large degree in many countries during the postwar period. In most industrial countries a very high level of employment was achieved and maintained. In Britain in particular, a high degree of general overfull employment developed. In the United States there was overfull employment in particular industries or in particular regions. Production was increased through working overtime, through attracting labor from nonproductive employment to industry, and, in Britain, through enlisting the services of housewives and retired people almost to the utmost limits of possibility. Having approached that limit, any further substantial increase in output was only possible through technological progress. The adoption of labor-saving machinery became imperative, apart altogether from any consideration of cuts in the cost of production, as the only means by which more goods could be produced in the absence of a possibility of securing more manpower. As the result of the prevailing shortage of labor, the pre-war attitude, which regarded the adoption of labor-saving methods as antisocial, gave way to the opposite view—that it is a matter of civic virtue to be able to produce more goods without having to use more labor, or to be able even to release labor for other purposes in spite of the increasing output.

One of the consequences of overfull employment has been the increase of real wages. Since time immemorial the level of wages has had a considerable influence on technological progress. Machine was able to compete with man more effectively whenever wages were high. A rise in real wages may make all the difference between some labor-saving device being profitable or otherwise. The higher the wages, the more inducement there is for managements to embark on costly research to invent labor-saving devices, and on even costlier capital expenditure to apply such devices.

Postwar monetary policy in Britain, in the United States, and in most industrial countries has been, a few intervals apart, distinctly expansionary. The fundamental change that has taken place in this respect, compared with pre-war monetary policies, as a result of which there was never enough capital and credit for the exploitation of all socially useful and commercially promising innovations, will be discussed in Chapter 13. Here let it be sufficient to point out that the work of inventors is now no longer frustrated by "tight-fisted bankers" refusing to finance the exploitation of their ideas. Industrialists have mostly been able since the war to raise the necessary funds and have been prepared to spend more liberally on research.

Steady demand for consumer goods has provided yet further encouragement to technological progress since the war. The growing belief that the ups and downs of the dreaded business cycle are now a matter of the past, and that governments are now committed to the maintenance of full employment, has encouraged industrial firms to take a long view by spending considerable amounts on research, even if they could not expect to derive any benefit from it for years to come. The increase in the purchasing power of the lower-income groups has provided the assurance of expanding markets. This assurance has enabled industry to mass-produce goods which in the past could not be produced in large quantities, because only rich and well-to-do people could afford them. The possibility of mass production provided commercial justification for costly research leading to automation.

Additional stimulus to spending on research and to the exploitation of its results has been provided by the almost uninterrupted rise in prices since the war. It has greatly reduced the risk of being unable to market the increased volume of manufactures at a reasonable profit, as a result of a downward trend of prices.

The expansion of consumer demand has been largely the result of the high level of employment, the development of social services, and the equalitarian trend of taxation, causing a decline of the propensity to save and increase of the propensity to consume. In addition, consumer demand has also received a powerful stimulus through the popularization of instalment business. Most of the additional consumer demand thereby created has affected consumer durable goods whose manufacture lends itself to automation, provided that the volume of demand makes their production in long series possible and justifies the capital expenditure involved in the re-equipment of the works. The increase of the demand resulting from the postwar expansion of instalment credits has made it necessary to expand plants, and this has provided opportunities for installing in the new wing the most up-to-date equipment without having to scrap existing equipment possessing a useful life for some years to come.

Before World War II, government intervention in the sphere of research was in most countries largely confined to the requirements of national defense. There would have been strong opposition to the spending of large amounts of public money on research the results of which would have stood to benefit private firms. Since World War II, governments have been spending a fair amount of public funds for such purposes. This has helped technological progress to no slight extent.

There has been a growing realization of the importance of scientific and technological research since World War II. Technology has come into fashion. Governments have been encouraged in their policy of intervention by evidence that public opinion has become increasingly conscious of it, and favorable to it.

Pressure of circumstances arising from the "cold war" has also largely contributed toward the advancement of research, leading to technological progress in general and progress in automation in particular. Its stimulating effect has been similar to that of the desire for national survival during the war. Even though the general public has been unaware of the significance of the competition between the two rival groups of powers in the technological sphere, many statesmen, administrators, industrial leaders, scientists, and engineers have duly realized that the survival of their country and of the free world has come to depend largely on their ability to hold their own in this sphere.

There is reason to believe that never in history has there been such a unique combination of circumstances favoring technological progress. In such a situation it would have been most extraordinary if spectacular progress had not been made. Beyond doubt the appearance of a number of first-rate scientists and technologists in many countries has greatly helped automation after World War II. Their appearance during a period in which circumstances favored progress has not, however, been sheer coincidence. But for the favorable circumstances, a good many of them would never have been given the chance to prove their worth. Their ideas might have fallen on sterile ground; it might have been impossible to apply them commercially. Financial limitations might even have deprived them of the chance of pursuing their research.

Many postwar inventions have given rise to entirely new industries. Having to start from scratch, these industries were not handicapped by the deadweight of obsolete equipment. They were in a position to apply the latest machinery, instead of having to decide whether or not to scrap the existing plant, or to strike a not very satisfactory compromise by supplementing the obsolete plant with automatic equipment. The demand for automatic equipment by the new industries has largely contributed toward the progress of automation since the end of the war.

The "cold war" accelerated the progress of automation, not only through creating urgent and imperative arms requirements, but also through stimulating competition between the rival groups of powers in the field of civilian production. Even on the dubious assumption that the slogan of "peaceful coexistence" is not merely a screen behind which Soviet Russia is preparing world conquest through peaceful penetration, it has become a matter of vital importance for the democratic countries not to allow themselves to be outpaced by the Communist block in technological progress.

The time lag between progress in the sphere of pure science and the technological application of its findings has been considerably reduced since World War II. Scientists and inventors no longer need to work solely or mainly for the sake of posthumous fame.

CHAPTER THREE

LIMITS OF AUTOMATION

THE progress of automation has been far from even within any one country. In some industries it has been truly spectacular. Such instances deservedly received much publicity, which conveyed the impression that technological progress has opened up practically unlimited possibilities. Not only the lay public but even many experts, who ought to know better, were inclined to generalize from such outstanding instances. Hence the widespread expectations of the development of a fully automated society within a relatively short time.

Yet automation has limits beyond which it cannot proceed. The whereabouts of these limits are the subject of much controversy among experts. It must be remembered that instances of automation which were considered inconceivable yesterday have now been accomplished, so that we cannot absolutely rule out the chances of today's impossibility becoming tomorrow's reality. The ultimate extent of automation is largely a matter of opinion. There is an almost equally wide scope for differences of opinion in respect to the pace at which automation is likely to progress. If even scientists and technologists disagree, we laymen are bound to find ourselves largely in the realm of conjectures. Nor is the study of the economic, financial, commercial and social limitations to the progress of automation an exact science. Without attempting to arrive at any too-definite conclusions, we propose to try to indicate, however, the factors that are liable to slow down or check the progress of automation in various spheres.

In the technological sphere scientists and engineers have to solve many difficult problems to ensure further progress of automation. In particular the problems of automatic handling of materials and of the automatic assembly of parts are in many industries very intractable. Conversion from batch production to continuous production appears at present impossible in many industries. But, as we pointed out in Chapter One, fifty years ago oil and chemical industries too employed batch-production systems. They were the first to solve the problem of the continuous flow of goods from process to process. The Ford works at Cleveland and Renaults in France have progressed a long way towards a solution of continuous flow in the motor industry. In Britain Sargrove has succeeded in creating a system of continuous automatic production of radio sets. So in many instances it was found that the limits to flow production are by no means impossible to overcome.

Needless to say, the acquisition of the necessary knowledge, and its application, are bound to be gradual. Progress towards full automation can only be achieved through trial and error in many industries. It is slowed down, among other causes, by the inadequate number of design engineers familiar with advanced mathematics. There is a shortage of prototype makers, production engineers, quality controllers, and other specialists.

Automatic equipment cannot be produced unless and until sufficient people qualified to design and build it become available. And even if its production becomes technically possible, it is not likely to be installed by any firm until the necessary specialized workers who are able to operate it and service it also become available, or at any rate until there are reasonable prospects for such manpower to become available in the very near future. Progress of automation is bound to be limited by the pace at which workers are upgraded to be qualified for operating automatic equipment. It may take half a generation before these shortages can be made good even with the aid of the best training schemes.

One of the major technico-commercial handicaps is that in most industries automatized machinery is only suitable for production in long series. Owing to the high cost of its installation and of its adjustment, it is not a commercial proposition to apply automatic equipment unless there is a possibility of mass-producing the same product over a fairly long period. Managements must be satisfied with the prospects that the profit derived from its reduced operating cost will pay for the capital expenditure, if the machinery has to undergo a costly adjustment for the sake of producing different goods. The risk of a change in public taste, necessitating an adjustment of the machinery soon after its installation, discourages managements from introducing automation. It is a task for the technologists to devise automatic machinery which is capable of producing a number of different goods that could be varied according to requirements, or, at any rate, which could be adjusted at a low cost. Sargrove has solved the problem in respect to radio production. But in most other industries no solution is within sight at the time of writing. Even so, a solution may be only a matter of time.

On the other hand, technical limitations are in some respects permanent. Electronic control devices have to be supplemented by human inspection of the finished product. Where judgment or taste is involved, human brains will always remain indispensable. According to Sir Henry Cohen, Professor of Medicine, Liverpool University, even in the largest computers there are only 75,000 tubes against 56,000 million nerve cells of the human brain.

Let us now turn to the commercial limitations of automation. The present high cost of the necessary installation is foremost among them. This is a temporary handicap, for popularization of the use of computers and other automatic machinery will make it possible to mass-produce them and to sell them at a much lower price. Already in some lines the price has been materially reduced in the course of a few years, so that it has become a commercial proposition to install them. The hiring of certain electronic equipment to smaller firms has also become commercially feasible.

A substantial handicap is the existence of a costly out-of-date plant. It is, of course, much more difficult to decide to scrap this plant and replace it by modern automatic equipment than to equip a new factory or an extension with automatic equipment. Fortunately from the point of view of progress, the persistent demand for increased output and the limitation of additional manpower available for that purpose often compel industrial firms to resort to automation even at the cost of scrapping their costly plant. As we pointed out in the last chapter, scarcity of labor has its uses from this point of view. But it remains none the less true that the existence of old plant constitutes a handicap to automation in industrialized countries. The rate at which existing plant can be replaced, in the absence of any compelling or tempting motive, as and when wear and tear makes this necessary, is very slow. Even in the United States one out of every five machines is, according to Diebold, over twenty years old, and 43 per cent over ten years old. In the absence of decisions to replace machinery long before it has completed its useful life, it would take many years before industry could become thoroughly automated even in the United States, especially as the above proportions include new industries which are, of course, thoroughly modern.

Replacement of plant is not the only capital expenditure involved in automation of existing works. There is also the high cost of replanning production system or routine. It is a mistake to imagine that all that is needed is to add some automatic contraption to the existing system. As was pointed out in Chapter Two, the entire process has to be replanned in order to get the best advantage out of automation. Indeed in many instances automation would not be possible without drastic readjustment of the process. All this requires much research and experimenting, the cost of which has to be added to that of the actual investment in new plant. It constitutes an additional deterrent. What is more, in a number of known instances firms intending to carry out automation found that the preliminary reorganization secured such substantial economies that they decided not to proceed after all with automation.

Conservatism on the part of boards of directors is one of the causes of the relatively slow progress in automation. The law of inertia is liable to assert itself, unless the boards happen to have some dynamic members who succeed in carrying with them the less go-ahead elements. Firms which can make substantial profits with the aid of existing methods of production are naturally reluctant to embark on heavy capital expenditure. During periods of boom and inflation it is usually possible to work profitably without having to aim at a maximum of efficiency. Firms in quasi-monopolistic positions are tempted to adopt a conservative line, and so are producers of new goods with assured markets.

Paradoxical as it may sound, the electronics industry in the United States was until recently, according to Diebold, very backward in this respect. "Like the shoemaker's children who are often the least well shod," he remarked when addressing a conference of the electronics industry, "or the doctors who consider their health last, the electronics industry is just beginning to apply automatic control to its own manufacturing operations. More than three-quarters of its employees work in production jobs." (The high proportion of maintenance staff compared with production staff is the measure of automation.) Automatic control devices for other industries are largely hand-assembled and hand-tested by the firms which produce and supply them! This instance shows the degree of conservatism that remains to be overcome, even in the most modern industry of the most progressive country, before automation can achieve really widespread application. According to more recent information, the American electronics industry made in fact considerable progress toward automation during the middle fifties. On the other hand, the automation of factories producing automatic transfer machines is handicapped by the wide variety of requirements to which they have to cater. Relatively low cost of human labor in many countries is a very effective handicap to automation. This limit is liable to be affected by the rising standard of living. For instance, in postwar Japan automation is not limited by low wages to anything like the extent it would have been limited before World War II. Relations between automation and the wage level are reciprocal. In so far as automation raises wages, higher wages up to a point enable industry to proceed with automation. If, however, the cost of producing automatic equipment increases to a higher degree than the cost of labor that is to operate the re-equipped factories, then the rise in wages does not affect the limits of automation.

Managements are by no means alone in displaying conservatism in the face of automation. Its progress to the limits made possible by the present state of technology is handicapped to a much higher degree by the attitude of employees and their unions. Even many of those who realize that the fears that automation may cause general unemployment are grossly exaggerated feel that its adoption is detrimental to their immediate bargaining position and scarcity value. In many instances they either resisted the introduction of automatic devices, or they insisted on feather-bedding and make-work arrangements. The cost of such arrangements and the difficulties of negotiating them constitute a strong deterrent from the employer's point of view.

The consumer, too, has his say. Industrial firms fear that there would be consumer resistance to standardized products. Moreover, in many instances the goods or their packings have to be changed in order to make them suitable for the new production methods. There is always the risk that even a small change may act as a deterrent to would-be buyers.

There are also financial factors tending to delay automation. Under the existing fiscal system in Britain, the United States, and other industrial countries, there is not sufficient inducement in the form of tax concessions to encourage industrial firms to devote large amounts to the re-equipment of their works with automatic devices. Moreover, high taxation tends to drain the financial resources of industries and of investors. It does not leave sufficient risk capital and it discourages the propensity to take risk in circumstances in which the investor has to stand the full burden of a loss but is only allowed to retain a fraction of a gain.

Until comparatively recently the scarcity of monetary resources constituted the most important handicap to technological progress. Although the monetary system is more flexible today and it is easier to obtain bank credit than it was in the old days, risk capital, on the other hand, is less easily obtainable. Moreover from time to time even bank credits for working capital have to be curtailed to correct an overinflated situation. So even in existing circumstances the financial limitations to automation should not be overlooked.

Economic factors working against too rapid automation include the self-regulating character of the system. If automation should ever proceed at a pace at which it would create large-scale unemployment, it would generate a deflationary depression which would discourage any further progress. The cost of this automatic brake would be very high. There is, however, very little danger, even in the United States, of large-scale technological unemployment so long as the economy continues to expand.

Another automatic economic brake which is liable to slow down the pace of automation is the possibility of development of scarcity of materials, or of electric power. As a result of a sudden increase in production brought about by automation, bottlenecks may develop from time to time and expansion of production would thus be temporarily checked. Unless the use of atomic energy for power generation makes good progress, the prospects of widespread automation will be far from encouraging.

These and other considerations must be allowed for before

risking optimistic forecasts about the likelihood of "general" automation in the lifetime of the present generation. In any event, there are many industries in which the automation of actual production has no scope, or only a limited scope.

Industries which are eminently suitable for automation, such as oil refinery, chemicals, flour milling, etc., are already largely automated, and there remains little scope for their further automation. Many other industries offer fair possibilities, but there are many others which do not lend themselves to automation to any considerable degree, if at all. Various estimates have been put forward about the proportion of industry that is liable to become automated, but, owing to the uncertainty of future inventions, such estimates are mere guesses. Lists of unsuitable industries published a few years ago have already been disproved by events. For instance, there is in the United States, and to some extent in other countries, a fair progress in the automation of agriculture, which was until recently near the bottom of the list of industries capable of being automated to any appreciable extent.

Even allowing for the probable removal or reduction of the various existing handicaps to automation, it is safe to assume that the total number of those directly affected will never be more than a small proportion of the total population of even the most highly industrialized country. Diebold is right in ridiculing the grim picture, often presented not only in science fiction but also in serious writings on automation, of jobless and debased workers roaming the streets in a fully automated community, receiving even their relief vouchers from automatic machines. There are enough unsurmountable limitations to automation to safeguard mankind from such a nightmare ever becoming reality.

CHAPTER FOUR

AUTOMATION ECONOMICS

ALTHOUGH there is a growing literature on the technological, social and commercial aspects of automation, its broader economic aspects have received relatively little attention. The main reason for this is that most economists refuse to admit the existence of any specific economic problems arising from automation. They take the view that from an economic point of view there is nothing fundamentally new in the latest phase of industrial revolution. Technological progress is almost as old as mankind, and the difference made by the acceleration of its pace during recent years is, according to economists, merely one of degree. They feel that economic situations arising from automation are covered by economic theory in general and by recent literature on economic expansion in particular.

This attitude bears much similarity to the attitude taken by most economists in democratic countries during the years that preceded World War II. While in Germany "national-defense economics" had become an important branch of economic science, in the democratic countries its existence was ignored. The view was held that situations arising from rearmament and war could be dealt with adequately on the basis of the accepted body of economic doctrines. The result was that Germany entered World War II much better prepared in the economic field than her opponents. The latter

45

had to improvise and learn by trial and error, while Germany was in a position to apply solutions carefully thought out at leisure in pre-war days. The lesson of this experience should go some way toward making it obvious that closer study of automation economics in the democratic countries is essential.

There is a multitude of practical economic problems arising from automation which call for examination. In this chapter we are concerned, however, with the effect of automation on economic theory. It is arguable that, on the assumption that the extent or the rate of automation is likely to remain moderate, no such analysis is called for. In reality, from a theoretical point of view it is principles that matter, not the extent of their effect. In any case, we have no means of knowing what further technological inventions the future is likely to bring and at what rate they will come to be applied in industry. Among technological experts opinions are divided on the subject. A considerable number of experts believe in the possibility of a much higher degree of automation than what we have hitherto experienced. The economist is entitled to be skeptical, but he cannot claim to know more about the prospects of technological progress than do the physicists and technologists themselves. He cannot, therefore, rule out the possibility of a very considerable progress, and it is his duty to assume such a possibility, at any rate as a working hypothesis. The fact that, rightly or wrongly, many people believe in it constitutes a challenge to economists which they should not ignore.

Admittedly the effects of automation on production costs, on the quantity of output, on capital requirements, on the demand for labor, etc., are largely a matter of degree. This does not, of course, mean that, for that reason, such effects are not worth the closest attention of economists. There is, however, at least one respect in which automation is claimed to produce a fundamentally new situation which is not covered by the existing body of economic theory. An examination of this claim calls for a reconsideration of basic principles. It was first put forward by Peter F. Drucker, according to whom automation has changed the way in which output responds to changes in the relation between supply and demand.

Under the accepted economic theory the price mechanism by which supply and demand are brought into equilibrium functions not only through fluctuations of prices but also through the fluctuations of output. Any change in the relation between supply and demand sets into motion an automatic tendency toward adjustment through changes in the volume of supply and in the demand resulting from the changes in prices. Thus if there is an increase in demand for certain goods in relation to their supply, the result is a rise in their prices. This again tends to discourage demand and stimulate an increase in production. Conversely a fall in demand—or an increase in supply in excess of demand—tends to cause a fall in prices which again tends to encourage demand and to discourage production of the goods concerned. Were it not for the effect on output of fluctuations in demand, changes in prices would have to go much further before they are halted by their effect on demand.

According to Drucker, this system is liable to be affected considerably as a result of a wide adoption of automation. As he pointed out in an article entitled "The Promise of Automation" (*Harper's Magazine,* April 1955), production by automated industries responds to short-term economic fluctuations to a limited degree only. Automated factories are not likely to reduce their output immediately as soon as there is evidence of a fall in demand. What he means is that not only is the production schedule of the automated factory based on long series and not easily to be altered, but also that, owing to the increased relative importance of capital outlay (which includes also the cost of "re-thinking" the whole process of production and of training the necessary specialist staff) compared with current cost of production, it may not be worth while to alter pre-arranged production schedules. Automated firms may find it preferable to cut their prices rather than interfere with their production schedules.

Drucker emphasizes that the principle of the continuous flow which is the main characteristic of automated production, must apply not only in the technological sense but also in an economic sense.

The need for managements of automated factories to plan their output in such a way as to ensure continuity is also stressed by a practical businessman, Paul A. Just, Executive Vice-President of the Television Shares Management Corporation. In an address reprinted in the March 15, 1956 issue of the *Commercial and Financial Chronicle* of New York, he points out that, in non-automated factories, current assembly procedures are so designed that if the market for end products declines, then production can be cut back to meet the lessened demand. "To a great extent, however," he observed, "this would be virtually impossible in an automated factory. The market must be positively established and its future course accurately plotted. Then, engineers design the production process to exact market specifications. Wide deviations from the market estimate would spell tremendous losses for the company. . . . This stems from the great expense involved in installing complex machinery capable of handling functions on a totally automatic basis.

"This means, then, a totally new approach must be taken by the businessman of the future. And, of course, it is going to place greater responsibilities on management's shoulders. Management cannot engage in guesswork in determining what market exists for its product. It may even mean that markets will actually have to be created by the company first. Once management has established certain patterns and formulae for harmonizing market and production, then we will have arrived at one of the great future benefits of automation. With an assured market, the automated factory will have guaranteed production for a set period of time. This means employment stabilization."

In the face of a prolonged or substantial setback in demand it would, of course, become necessary eventually to alter production schedules. There is much less likelihood, however, of an immediate response of the output of automated factories to changed supply-and-demand relations. This would mean that a fall in prices would have to proceed much further in order to stimulate the increase of demand necessary to absorb the unchanged high flow of supply. In other words, since supply will not act as a shock-absorber to the same extent as before automation, prices have to assume increased responsibility for adjustment. Drucker's theory, if it is valid, tends to reduce the validity of one of the major principles of classical economics.

The question is whether this stabilizing effect of automation on supply is not liable to be offset by its stabilizing effect on demand. The concluding sentence of Paul Just's remarks quoted above does, in fact, indicate that employment as well as output tends to be stable in automated industries. Diebold expressed views in the same sense when giving evidence before the Congressional Subcommittee on Automation on October 27, 1955. He pointed out that, with the decrease in labor cost and increase in capital costs—which must be carried regardless of the level of output—the advantages of labor layoffs will diminish. Output will more likely be maintained. "As a result, changes in demand will, in all likelihood, affect prices rather than output and employment." This means that, in so far as automation results in the maintenance of the output in face of temporary recessions, it not only maintains the supply of goods but also consumer purchasing power, by maintaining employment. A recession means a fall in the output of non-automated industries, causing a decline in supplies and also in incomes. As far as automated industries are concerned, however, both supplies and incomes would remain relatively stable.

On the face of it, the above consideration may appear to invalidate the theory that, as a result of automation, a business recession must lead to a sharper fall in prices in the absence of a decline in output. In fact, in considering the validity of this theory, we must distinguish between the state of affairs during the transitional period and the final situation created after the end of the transitional period. In so far as automation is proceeded with during a period of depression, its main purpose is labor-saving, so that it entails the immediate dismissal of all redundant employees. But automation achieved during boomlike conditions—such as have prevailed almost continuously since the war—usually means that managements do not take full advantage of the labor-saving possibilities of the new automatic equipment. They are liable to retain more workers than are strictly needed, partly to avoid trouble with the unions and partly because, owing to the prevailing scarcity of labor, they are inclined to "hoard" manpower. The reduction in cost of production achieved through automation leaves them with a sufficient margin of profit to be able to afford such a wasteful use of manpower. The prevailing high level of taxation may lead them to prefer to spend a large part of their increased profits on "hoarding" labor in anticipation of increased manpower requirements that may result from a further expansion in their output. Moreover, they may be reluctant to assist their rivals by releasing manpower.

Once, however, a recession has set in, these firms will seek to cut down their costs by dismissing their redundant workers. Dismissals through redundancy, which normally should have taken place immediately after the adoption of automatic equipment, are in fact deferred until the first recession that follows the change. With the aid of their new automatic equipment, the firms are then able to maintain their high output in spite of the dismissal of their redundant workers. This means that the maintenance of their output at pre-recession level is accompanied by an accentuation of a decline in demand as a result of the deferred appearance of techno-logical unemployment in automated industries. In such con-ditions, the theory that automation entails an adjustment of the supply-and-demand position, through a supplementary fall in prices necessitated by the rigidity of the output, is valid to a considerable degree.

It may take some time before the unnatural state of affairs created by the feather-bedding, during a boom, of workers who have become redundant as a result of automation is corrected and these workers become properly absorbed in the economy. In the long run the automated firms may gradually reduce their manpower to the lower requirements of their automated factories by not replacing workers who reach the retiring age. Once that situation has been achieved, employment will become more stable as a result of the operation of completed automation. This means that after the end of the transitional period the stability of output of the automated industries will be accompanied by a corresponding stability of demand resulting from the stability of employment. In such circumstances the rule laid down by Drucker and Diebold, that, under automation, a supplementary decline in prices assumes the role hitherto played by a decline in output, will cease to operate.

The question is how long the transitional period is likely to continue. Given the political and industrial balance of power between employers and employees and the general economic climate arising from a high level of employment and high taxation, it may take many years before the labor-saving character of automatic equipment comes to be utilized to the full extent for the purpose of saving labor. Moreover, while in any individual industry the transitional period may come to an end sooner or later, for the community as a whole it may never come to an end. Even if all the existing inventions achieve full application in all industries which lend themselves to automation, there is bound to be an endless succession of new inventions which will further widen the scope for automation. Their application will set in train new transitional periods. In the same way as electrification is a never-ending process, automation is likely to continue indefinitely. To the extent to which its progress gives rise to new transitional periods the rule concerning the relative role of output and prices during early periods of recession is liable to operate. Even if a prolonged depression should accelerate the pace at which employment in automated industries is reduced to the level determined by technological requirements, the progress of automation following on the recovery from such depression would once more be accompanied by circumstances giving rise to a fresh transitional period between the installation of labor-saving equipment and the saving of labor to the limit of its potentialities.

This means that although the theoretical rule described above applies during the transitional period only, it is of fundamental economic importance because of the likelihood of continuous transitional periods. It deserves, therefore, the attention of theoretical economists, even if its significance is probably less than is assumed by Diebold and Drucker. What they appear to have left out of consideration is that after the end of the transitional period the operation of completed automation tends to stabilize both supply and demand during a period of moderate recession.

Hitherto we have been dealing with the effect of automation on current output. Automation is, however, also liable to affect the behavior of entrepreneurs in respect to capital investment in the face of a business recession. The continuous flow of output that characterizes automation is not confined to the current output of consumer goods but applies equally to the output of capital goods required for the installation of automatic equipment. According to Paul Just, employment stabilization through automation means that having achieved a known market, a known rate of production, and a fixed labor force, industrial investment plans are also brought to an even keel. "Wide fluctuations in demand for capital will be eliminated, which of course, will tend to regularize one of the most sensitive areas of our entire economy. The raising of capital in other words will not be dependent on, or contribute to, boom or bust cycles."

Drucker put forward a much more effective argument in support of his view on the stabilizing effect of automation.

He pointed out that it is impossible to proceed piecemeal with capital investment connected with automation, or to make its progress dependent on the business conditions of the moment. Once automation projects have been initiated they have to be completed. By this Drucker presumably means that while it is possible to cancel part of an order for a number of machine tools, it is not possible to cancel an order for a large transfer machine or for a large electronic computer, after its production has been initiated, without the complete loss of the cost that has already been incurred. It is for this reason that, according to Drucker, few American firms stopped their capital expenditure programs during the recessions of 1951 and 1954. Britain had the same experience during the disinflationary drive of 1955-1956.

The maintenance of stable employment and income in connection with capital expenditure during recessions occurring in the transitional period of automation tends to offset the effect of automation on prices through the maintenance of the output by automated factories. Although there are likely to be dismissals by automated factories during the transitional period, the effect of such dismissals on consumer demand and prices is moderated by the stability of capital goods industries due to the continuous character of automation investment.

Postwar experience in respect to the stability of investment in automatic equipment during periods of moderate recessions calls in question the validity of the Keynesian theory regarding the relative importance of investment. Amidst postwar inflation it has become evident that the relative importance of consumer spending is much greater than Keynesian economics assumed it to be on the basis of inter-war experience. With the realization that the relative importance of investment is less than Keynesian economics assumed it to be, not only during periods of inflation, but also during periods of recession, the need for a reconsideration of that part of Keynesian economics has become imperative.

Owing to the exaggerated importance attached to investment as the dynamic factor determining business trends, disinflationary drives in the postwar period in Britain, and to some extent in other countries, assumed overwhelmingly the form of a discouragement of investment. This policy is far from helpful from the point of view of the progress of automation. Even though projects which have already been initiated are proceeded with, fiscal disincentives and credit restrictions may discourage the initiation of new automation projects. Moreover the exaggeration of the relative importance of investment diverts attention from the responsibility of excessive wage demands for the accentuated inflation and for the resulting delays of investment in general and of automation in particular. Unions are inclined to make full use of the prevailing fashion in economic theory for the reinforcement of new arguments in favor of wage demands, on the ground that it is not higher wages but excessive capital investment that is to blame for inflation. Their wage demands, encouraged by the exaggeration of the relative importance of investment, lead to inflation which the government seeks to check through one-sided measures directed against investment.

The world owes Keynes a great deal of gratitude. Were it not for his influence on economic thought automation would probably be held back by a restrictionist monetary policy. But much of what has been gained from his part in leading governments to adopt an expansionary and elastic monetary policy has been lost through another aspect of his influence on post-war economic thought, as a result of which the effects of wage increases on inflation and, through inflation, on the government's attitude toward investment, have come to be underrated. In the light of postwar experience, and in view of the requirements of a speedy progress of automation, it is of the utmost importance that economists should reconsider their one-sided emphasis of the relative importance of capital expenditure.

Owing to the rigidity of production schedules in automated industries, entrepreneurs are often unable to behave in the way they are supposed to behave according to classical theory, by adjusting their output immediately to changes in demand. On the other hand, Dr. Bowden drew attention, at the 1955 Conference of the Institute of Management, to an effect of automation which, he claims, points in exactly the opposite direction. He said that classical economists overlooked the fact that it takes a long time for entrepreneurs to study an industrial situation in detail and to evaluate the possible effects of alternative decisions. The assumption of classical economists that information on which entrepreneurial decisions are based was freely and rapidly available is incorrect. This is why, according to Dr. Bowden, much of their theory seems to lack all connection with realities of the world in which we live.

There is bound to be a considerable time lag between actual changes in the situation and prospects, the realization of these changes and of the need to alter production plans in consequence, and the actual elaboration of alternative plans. In practice, these delays largely vitiate the theoretical rules on which entrepreneurs are supposed to act. The electronic computer and other automatic devices have gone a long way towards reducing such delays, and it seems reasonable to expect that the more general adoption of such devices by managements will tend to reduce friction in economic adjustments. Automation, so far from contributing toward the demise of the Economic Man, may contribute toward his revival or rehabilitation.

There is no real contradiction between the findings of Bowden and of Drucker. The former has in mind the automated management of industry in general while the latter refers to the automated factory. Both points are interesting from the point of view of pure theory. They would be well worth following up.

This book is concerned with practical economic problems arising from automation, but the author is anxious to draw the attention of theoretical economists to the need for investigating the theoretical implications of the recent and prospective technological developments. The present chapter has no such ambitious aims. It is merely intended to provide a few instances of such theoretical implications in the hope of making economists realize that there is such a thing as automation economics.

CHAPTER FIVE

SOME PRACTICAL ECONOMIC PROBLEMS

WE OUTLINED in the last chapter some theoretical economic considerations arising in connection with automation. They were only touched upon briefly, as this book is primarily concerned with practical economic problems. There is indeed a multitude of such problems to be considered. Hardly any aspect of economic life is likely to be unaffected, or is likely to remain unaffected by automation. Its effects on production, employment, prices and wages, will influence the standard of living, the monetary situation, the balance of payments, the fiscal system, the raw-materials position, and even such spheres as foreign-exchange policy or national-defense economy. Nor is the impact one-sided. Various economic tendencies are liable to react on the progress of automation, as well as being affected by it.

(1) Its effect on employment is probably the most extensively explored economic aspect of automation. Most discussions of this subject are confined, however, to the examination of the probable extent of technological unemployment. Yet the effect of automation on non-technological unemployment also deserves attention. An unbiased survey of the prospects should recognize the possibility of unemployment through "bottlenecks"—shortages of materials or of fuel and

power—resulting from sudden expansion of production through automation. Above all, unemployment through obsolescence deserves far more attention than it has received, especially because it is the antidote to the poison of exaggerated fears of technological unemployment. The extent to which industries which are left behind in the "automation race" are liable to find themselves at a disadvantage does not appear to have been realized sufficiently. This is because, under the inflationary conditions prevailing since the war, the more progressive firms have so far preferred to use the benefits of automation for increasing their profits or for conceding wage claims rather than for cutting prices. It is because of this circumstance that the less progressive firms have been allowed to exist. But it is well to realize that they only exist on sufferance. The moment the progressive producers decide to adjust prices to their lower costs of production, their less progressive rivals will be competed out of existence.

(2) A number of economic problems arise from the increase of output through automation. There is, of course, an extensive literature on economic expansion, including some recent works of considerable importance. But these are primarily concerned with normal growth, and do not specifically investigate the wide range of economic problems arising from a sudden and spectacular increase of output through automation. It has been suggested by "depression economists" that, owing to the delay in the distribution of profits, an increasing trend of production means a deflationary time lag, because it is accompanied by an increase in profits. One of the objects of the present book is to show that this theory is unfounded and that the time lag involved in expanding production, so far from being deflationary, has been, in the conditions prevailing during most of the time since the end of

World War II, strongly inflationary. About this more will be said in Chapter 9.

Automation may bring about a substantial increase in output even after full employment has been reached. This result depends on whether automation aims primarily at the same output with the aid of less manpower or at a higher output with the aid of the same manpower. It will be seen that, amidst conditions prevailing during the fifties, automation aimed primarily at a higher output. During a period of depression producers would endeavor to reduce costs and would not dare to increase their output even at a lower cost per unit. During boomlike conditions, however, the main object is to meet increasing demand by an increase of the output. As we saw in the last chapter, it is a matter of great importance that the increased output of automated industries is less liable to fluctuate through short-term changes in business conditions than the output of non-automated industries.

(3) The effect of automation on the price level needs careful analysis. It is all but generally assumed that automation should mean a decline in the price level. This mistaken conclusion is reached on the ground that producers are likely to pass on to the consumers at least part of the lower cost of production in the form of price cuts. It is the task of Automation Economics to balance the various considerations against each other and to arrive at a conclusion whether, in balance, automation is inflationary or deflationary. There can be no simple answer. The effect depends largely on the circumstances; it is different according to whether the economic climate in which automation operates is inflationary or deflationary.

(4) The way in which the benefit derived from lower cost through automation is shared out between the interests con-

cerned gives rise to economic problems of considerable importance. The arguments in favor of each of these interests grossly oversimplify a highly involved situation. If the workers' claims were to be satisfied in full by increasing wages and/or reducing working hours to the full exent of the saving of costs effected by the new machinery, very wide differentials would develop between wages in various industries. If the demand for using the cuts in cost entirely in lowering prices were to be complied with, it would mean that the less efficient firms would be competed out of existence. If the benefit were to be allowed to increase profits to be distributed to shareholders, there might not be sufficient addition to consumer demand to absorb the additional goods to be produced. If all additional profits were to be ploughed back into the firms, it would provide opportunities for "take-over bids." The solution lies obviously in a compromise by which the benefit is to be shared between workers, enterprise, shareholders and consumers. It is mainly the proportion of their respective participation that must be a matter of argument.

(5) Another set of questions of importance is whether automation is likely to increase capital requirements materially, if at all, and, if so, how the additional requirements are to be met. The answer depends largely on the rate at which automation progresses. If it does not exceed the normal rate of wear and tear, then all that will happen is that as and when machinery becomes due to be replaced it will be replaced by automatic equipment, and new plants will be equipped with automatic machinery. But the accelerated pace of the progress of technology is likely to make it necessary to change the equipment more frequently in order to keep pace with rivals. Allowing for this, the question whether the amount of capital invested per employee will increase

could be answered in the affirmative, were it not for the reduction in the cost of production of capital equipment. What matters is whether capital equipment *per unit of output* is reduced sufficiently to make it commercially profitable to replace the equipment whenever technological progress results in the appearance of better equipment.

Further economic problems presented by the question of capital investment are in the sphere of financing any additional requirements. This raises questions relating to monetary policy, the rate of saving and investment, fiscal methods of incentive or disincentive, and the supply of risk capital.

(6) Changes in the terms of trade—the cost of imports in terms of exports—may result from automation and are liable to affect the balance of payments. Automation has not nearly as wide a scope in agriculture and mining as in manufacturing industries. Consequently it is liable to lower the cost of manufactures to a larger extent than those of raw materials and food. During a period of rising prices it may keep down the rise in manufacture prices compared with the rise in raw-material prices. Indeed, automation is likely to stimulate demand for materials and accentuate the rise in their prices. This means that, for those reasons alone, the terms of trade may move against industrial countries, which may have to export more in order to pay for the same quantity of imports.

(7) Automation will create new kinds of foreign-exchange problems. Through its effect on the balance of payments it may affect the gold reserves. Relative progress of automation in one country may upset the fundamental equilibrium on which the stability of fixed exchanges rests. It affects the "purchasing-power parities," and may lead to devaluations or revaluations.

(8) Problems relating to business cycles figure promi-

nently among the economic problems of automation. It is widely believed that the pre-war type of automatic business cycle has been superseded by the postwar type of business cycle, largely induced by official policies aimed at reversing an excessive expansion or contraction of business or an unwanted trend of prices. But it remains to be seen whether the old-type business cycle is really dead. What matters is to find an answer to the question whether or not automation adds to the elements of instability in the business situation, or whether it tends to increase or reduce the difficulty of maintaining a balanced economy.

(9) In the sphere of monetary policy the authorities have to solve the problem of reconciling two conflicting requirements. On the one hand, they have to ensure a sufficiency of financial resources to enable industry to proceed with automation and to enable consumers to buy the increased volume of output resulting from it. On the other hand, they have to endeavor to counteract the inflationary effects of an increase in investment connected with automation, and of an unduly rapid expansion in the aggregate cost of production. To reconcile the two conflicting considerations it may be necessary to create conditions favorable to increasing saving to a sufficient extent to provide for the increased capital requirements, without overdoing it to an extent that prevents producers from selling their increased output.

(10) Automation may have a detrimental effect on the raw-material supply position. By increasing production and consumption to a very large extent, it may lead to the exhaustion of the sources of irreplaceable materials, such as metals. It will be a race between increase in production, calling for more and more raw materials, and the discovery of new mineral deposits or other raw-material resources or the

invention of substitutes. Supplies are liable to become depleted before alternative supplies can be developed. A rapid rate of automation is likely to be accompanied therefore by the development of frequent bottlenecks, holding up the expansion of production. This aspect of the subject presents yet another set of new and complicated economic problems.

(11) Fiscal means figure prominently among the devices with which governments have to encourage automation. The need for tax concessions to encourage capital expenditure is above controversy. On the other hand there is conflict between the need for reversing the trend of taxation aiming at equalitarianism in order to provide inducement for superior skill, and the need for an equal distribution in order to ensure markets for the increased output. Savings too have to be encouraged largely by fiscal concessions.

(12) There is also a set of problems arising from the controversy about the degree and nature of government intervention arising from the economic aspects of automation. In this respect ideological dogmatism for or against official controls over economic activities is liable to influence the arguments.

(13) Although problems of wage policy arising from automation are of great social significance, they have also far-reaching economic implications. Apart from problems relating to the general level of wages, there are many difficult questions concerning wage differentials between various categories of labor. There is also the question of the reciprocal effect of rising wages and progress in automation. The former tends to make the latter profitable in given circumstances, while automation makes for higher wage levels.

(14) The economic effect of automation on underdeveloped countries deserves careful consideration. They have the advantage of being able to adopt the latest equipment with-

out having to scrap existing equipment and without being handicapped by the existence of obsolete factory buildings. Regarded from this point of view alone, it must appear that automation stands a better chance to progress in new countries than in old ones. But there are other considerations. Foremost among them is lack of capital resources, whether in the form of capacity to produce machinery or in the form of financial savings with which to finance capital expansion. Moreover, the existence of cheap and plentiful labor also tends to handicap automation. After all, the necessary machinery is not introduced for the sake of the pleasure of seeing the wheels go round automatically, but for the sake of economizing in cost.

(15) Economic considerations of national defense will have to be re-examined in the light of automation. In that sphere automation is even more imperative than in the civilian sphere, in the interests of our survival. A considerable degree of automation would enable the democratic countries to spend what is needed on defense without having to reduce the standard of living or even without preventing its further advance. Our potential enemies are, however, in a similar position. The rate of their industrialization and the resulting increase of their economic war potential has been accelerated by automation. It may be that the "cold war" will be won by the side which is in a position to make more rapid progress in this sphere. The democratic countries will have to maintain and even increase their superiority in the technological sphere in order to offset the advantage of the superior manpower of the Communist countries.

The above summary is by no means exhaustive, but it should give a general idea of the range and nature of the economic problems arising from automation. They will be examined in greater detail in the subsequent chapters.

CHAPTER SIX

PRODUCTION UNDER OVERFULL EMPLOYMENT

BEFORE analyzing the effects of automation on employment, we propose to give a brief account of the effects of overfull employment on production during the postwar period. This is necessary, in view of the popular feeling that automation is disadvantageous if it reduces, however slightly, the existing degree of employment. Although the observations in this chapter refer primarily to the situation created by overfull employment in Britain, there are indications that somewhat similar conditions tend to develop in other industrial countries of the free world. In the United States, for instance, areas of unemployment alternate with areas where there is an acute shortage of labor, so that there is in many industrial districts local overfull employment in spite of the continued existence of a relatively large number of unemployed in the country as a whole. In certain American industries there is overfull employment which tends to become accentuated whenever there is an expansion of business activity. Owing to inadequate mobility of labor, among other causes, it is not always easy for these industries to draw upon these manpower reserves, substantial as they are in theory.

A diversion from our main argument, to draw attention to the disadvantages of overfull employment is necessary be-

66

cause, once it is realized that scarcity of labor is not an advantage to the community, the possibility of its mitigation as a result of automation is likely to be looked upon in a different light. These disadvantages manifested themselves to some extent even in the United States and other industrial countries, although their extent was incomparably more moderate than in post-war Britain.

Full employment seems to have become largely an emotional issue which can no longer be discussed rationally. Anything that is likely to reduce the extent of employment is viewed with hostility by employees. This is only natural. They feel that employment is such a good thing that there could never be enough of it, let alone too much. Human nature being what it is, we should all like to possess a high scarcity value and a strong bargaining position. But some of us realize that our immediate personal interests in this respect are not necessarily identical with the public interest. Nor indeed are they necessarily identical with our long-term personal interests. For the considerable disadvantages to the community of overfull employment are liable to recoil sooner or later on those who appear to benefit for the moment from their scarcity value.

Occasionally some employer or politician or economist, exasperated by some flagrant abuse, expresses a wish for "a little unemployment" to put things right. Even though the term "little" is open to various interpretations, it is inconceivable that any of these people would go so far as to wish to return to large-scale unemployment in the pre-war sense. The state of affairs in which everybody who wants employment can be employed has immense advantages not only to the employees themselves but also to their employers who, after all, stand to lose through bad trade. It has great advantages for everybody who is in favor of preserving prosperity and the system of democratic freedom; for there can be no doubt that in existing circumstances a return of large-scale unemployment would mean the end of democracy.

Nor can there be any doubt that, if the choice were between overfull employment and large-scale unemployment, everybody would unhesitatingly choose the former. But under the influence of the disadvantages of overfull employment a large and increasing number of people have come to the conclusion that the correct solution lies somewhere between the two extremes. Where exactly it should be is a matter of opinion. It is, however, safe to assert that everybody, without exception, is in favor of a high level of employment.

The fact that we believe in a high level of employment should not, however, blind us to its disadvantages. Indeed it would be self-deception not to recognize that, to some extent at any rate, the beneficial effects of full employment are offset by its unfavorable effects. So long as full employment does not degenerate into overfull employment, its advantages are so overwhelming that the disadvantages are hardly worth mentioning. But in postwar Britain, where overfull employment has existed almost uninterruptedly over a number of years, the disadvantages attached to a high level of employment have been strongly in evidence. The United States and other industrial countries which may have had a foretaste of overfull employment, may learn by the British experience the disadvantages of having an overdose of it. One of the main theses of this book is that automation, while mitigating the evil effects of *overfull* employment, maintains and even increases the beneficial effects of *full* employment.

Overfull employment is a state of affairs in which the

number of vacancies exceeds the number of those seeking employment. The published statistics in Britain do not adequately indicate the true extent of overfull employment. On the one hand, the small proportion of unemployed that continued to exist throughout the postwar period consisted mostly of unemployables, or of people temporarily out of employment between two jobs, or of seasonally unemployed. On the other hand, statistics of vacancies only show registered vacancies, which are probably a bare fraction of the true number of jobs that are available. Many employers do not even trouble to register their vacancies with Labor Exchanges, because in existing conditions they consider it useless to do so. Hundreds of thousands of domestic servants, for instance, could easily find employment, but those who would like to employ them realize that there is not the slightest hope of finding suitable applicants through Labor Exchanges. If the true figures of unfilled jobs were available they would no doubt exceed many times the number of genuinely unemployed.

The following are the main disadvantages arising from overfull employment:

(1) Lack of inducement for workers to maintain a high productivity.

(2) Decline of industrial discipline.

(3) Frequency of irresponsible strikes.

(4) Deterioration of workmanship.

(5) Inflationary wage spiral.

(6) Unsatisfactory distribution of manpower.

One of the main causes of Britain's postwar difficulties has been that the incentive provided by the fear of dismissal and unemployment has in far too many cases not been replaced by the incentive of the desire to give a good day's work for a good day's pay. Lack of incentive and lack of discipline cause in many instances a marked deterioration in the quality of the goods produced. An equally important cause of slipshod workmanship is that there is less inducement for young workers to spend years of apprenticeship in learning their trade. They are now able to earn good wages as unskilled laborers, and do not consider it worth their while to acquire specialized training. In many instances skilled work is carried out by inadequately trained labor.

Overfull employment encouraged frequent "wildcat strikes." Admittedly the actual number of working days lost through strikes after World War II in Britain was incomparably smaller than during the corresponding period following World War I. But, then, under conditions of overfull employment and inflation it has been in the interests of the employers to settle wage claims, whether or not justified, in order to avoid stoppages. The consumer had to pay. With their order books full for some time ahead, employers were anxious to avoid strikes at almost any costs. Realization of this state of affairs stimulated excessive wage demands, of the kind that would have inevitably led to strikes during the interwar period. In view of the increased willingness of employers to meet demands regarding wages and working conditions, the number of working days lost through strikes since World War II has been unnecessarily large.

The result has been an inflationary wage spiral. It is of course arguable that, were it not for the ever-rising purchasing power of the masses of industrial workers, postwar prosperity would have been interrupted by cyclical crises. The wage spiral and the other disadvantages of overfull employment are often presented as being equivalent to an insurance premium the community has to pay to safeguard itself against business cycles. But other countries which did not have to put up with the disadvantages of overfull employment have been equally immune from cyclic crises. If automation should reduce overfull employment, the "insurance premium" would be smaller, and so would be the risk of a recession through disinflationary measures which the government would eventually feel compelled to adopt.

Yet another disadvantage of overfull employment has been the maldistribution of labor. Industries working at a high profit and anxious to increase their output can afford to pay very high wages to attract workers from less-well-paid occupations. The result is an acute shortage of labor in such occupations, even though it would be to the benefit of the community if they were adequately manned. Very often socially useless enterprise deprives socially useful enterprise of its manpower.

Had it not been for the progress of mechanization and, in more recent years, of automation, the above disadvantages of overfull employment would have been even more pronounced. Scarcity of labor would have been much more acute but for the extent to which human labor has been replaced by machine since the war. Moreover, as we pointed out above, but for technological progress the output would be well under the pre-war level. Nor would employers have been in a position to meet wage demands to the same extent, and there would have been many more strikes.

It seems reasonable to assume that, in the conditions existing during the postwar period, further automation would further mitigate the unfavorable consequences of overfull employment. But for the prospects of automation, a further accentuation of overfull employment would have to be expected as a result of the self-aggravating character of inflationary pressure fed by the wage spiral. Even allowing for further automation, it is by no means certain that it will make sufficient progress to neutralize altogether the gathering pressure of inflation. All that can be said is that automation will tend to mitigate the evil.

To the extent to which automation reduces or keeps down the extent of overfull employment, it is an unmitigated advantage, not only from the one-sided point of view of employers but also from that of the community as a whole. For it is evident that under conditions of overfull employment productive capacity is not used to the best advantage of the community. Automation contributes towards the increase in output, not only through its direct and obvious effect on productivity, but also through its indirect and less obvious, but none the less real, effect on overfull employment.

CHAPTER SEVEN

MUST AUTOMATION BRING UNEMPLOYMENT?

IN THE last chapter we sought to show that, if automation did no more than mitigate the degree of overfull employment that exists in Britain and, to a greater or less extent, in other industrial countries, it would do more good than harm, even from the point of view of the long-term interests of the industrial workers themselves. The present chapter will examine whether automation is likely to go beyond relieving overfull employment and whether it is likely to bring about large-scale unemployment. In this respect we are confronted with two diametrically opposite views. One of them was expressed, in its most extreme form, by Dr. Norbert Wiener in his book *The Human Use of Human Beings*. In the revised second edition of that book, published by Doubleday in 1954, he made the forecast that the unemployment that would be caused in the United States by automation would overshadow the experience of the thirties. This view found supporters, though in a less extreme form, among many labor union leaders and their followers within and outside the United States.

The other extreme has been voiced by the numerous enthusiasts of automation. In order to make out the strongest possible case against labor union resistance to automation, they do their utmost to minimize its possible adverse effects on employment. Most of their arguments are, on the whole, sound, so far as they go. But they only present one side of the picture. Both supporters and opponents of automation always have technological unemployment in mind—that is, dismissals through redundancy created by the installation of labor-saving equipment.

It is of course understandable that, under the influence of some isolated instances of staff reductions resulting from automation, the possibility of wholesale replacement of men by machines should dominate the minds of most people interested in the economic consequences of the system. Supporters of automation are, however, nearer the truth than its opponents when they seek to prove that, in the balance, technological unemployment is likely to be moderate. What they as well as the opposite camp overlook is that automation is liable to cause *nontechnological* unemployment. Nor has the possibility of *delayed* technological unemployment that may arise not immediately after the installation of labor-saving equipment, but only on the occasion of the next trade recession, been adequately examined.

Unemployment may be classified according to its causes into the following categories:

(1) Technological unemployment arises through the replacement of men by machines.

(2) Unemployment through bottlenecks arises through curtailment of production because of lack of raw materials, semi-products, fuel, electric power, transport facilities, or skilled labor in key positions.

(3) Unemployment through obsolescence arises through loss of markets as a result of being undersold by firms using more up-to-date equipment.

(4) Financial unemployment arises when production has to be curtailed through credit squeezes or other causes leading to inadequacy of financial resources, or to unduly high interest rates.

(5) Deflationary unemployment arises when deficiency of purchasing power leads to a decline in consumer demand for goods.

(6) Underinvestment unemployment arises from a decline in capital expenditure.

(7) Unemployment through rationalization arises as a result of redundancy through amalgamations of firms, or their reorganization on more efficient lines.

(8) Change of demand unemployment arises from changes in consumer tastes, or from a diversion of purchasing power in new directions, or from changes in production methods leading to changes in requirements of capital goods.

(9) Imported unemployment arises from loss of overseas markets through a decline of demand in other countries, through depression or import restrictions in the importing countries, or to an overvaluation of the currency of the exporting country, or to increased imports competing with the national products on the domestic market.

The term "technological unemployment" was coined by that greatest of wishful thinkers, Karl Marx, who believed that capitalism was doomed, among other reasons, because there was bound to be an increase in the amount of capital per head of labor employed in production, and that, deprived of earnings, the laborers would be unable to buy the output produced with the aid of the growing volume of capital.

The static theory, according to which there is only a certain amount of work to be done, and any labor-saving device is therefore bound to reduce the number of workers who can be employed for the execution of that work, may have been roughly correct during periods of decline, of prolonged stagnation, or of very slow expansion. In the thirties automation would undoubtedly have created technological unemployment in addition to the existing deflationary unemployment. Amidst the conditions then prevailing the new devices would have been used for reducing the total cost of the existing output, rather than for increasing the output at the same total cost.

Today automation operates against an entirely different monetary, economic, social and political background. In conditions such as prevailed most of the time during the postwar period, amidst an expanding economy accompanied by an inflationary trend, large-scale technological unemployment was virtually inconceivable, at any rate so long as the trend continued. Industrial firms were determined to increase their output on the assumption that the inflated demand was bound to continue indefinitely, or that at any rate the government could not possibly afford to allow the development of a recession of sufficient dimensions to cause large-scale unemployment. For years the production plans of many firms had been handicapped by scarcity of labor. They would now seize the opportunity of increasing their output while retaining their existing staffs which they would not dare to reduce for fear of being left without an adequate labor force for further expansion. There was "hoarding" of labor instead of resorting to redundancy dismissals.

Moreover there was usually strong and successful resistance by the unions and by their members to such attempts at dismissals of redundant workers as occured. Frequently they insisted on "feather-bedding" and make-work practices in order to prevent dismissals, in spite of the reduced requirements of labor resulting from the installation of labor-saving equipment. Only firms which were able to use the new machinery for increasing their output instead of for reducing their labor cost could proceed with automation unhampered. Firms which did not expect to be able to sell a larger volume of goods had to abstain, in many instances, from automation aimed at labor-saving, because in the circumstances of the postwar period labor refused to be saved. It is probable, however, that in the large majority of companies there was no such resistance to automation, because it could be affected without redundancy dismissals.

Although automation tends to reduce direct labor requirements for an unchanged output, it tends to create employment in other directions. Until the system has reached maturity there is bound to be an additional demand for capital equipment to replace the old machinery. Owing to the more intensive use of machinery by several small shifts, it is likely to wear out more quickly. In any case, new inventions are liable to make the automatic equipment obsolete in a relatively short time. Larger profits earned through the reduction of cost per unit of output enables the firms to replace obsolescent equipment earlier.

The electronics industry itself provides a fair amount of new employment. It is an expanding industry with wide possibilities. In his evidence before the Congressional Subcommittee on Economic Stabilization Reuther pointed out, however, that "even automation is being automated," so that employment in the electronics industry is not expanding at anything like the same rate as its output. Between 1947 and 1952 its output increased by 275 per cent, but the number of its employees increased by 40 per cent only.

On the other hand, new industries, which owe their existence to automation, have come into being. Apart from the production of atomic energy and of isotopes, which could not have been achieved by hand methods and close human contact, the Congressional Subcommittee's Report on Automation and Technological Change quotes the instance of polyethylene (a new and very useful product increasingly employed in everyday household items) which could not have been produced without applying automation methods. The number of similar examples is likely to grow in the course of time. Automation will create new industries in which the use of direct human labor would be too dangerous, or which call for a degree of precision that is beyond human capacity. Even after allowing for such possibilities, however, the Congressional Report pointed out that "it would be unwise to overemphasize the employment potentials in these new industries and assume that their growth will be sufficient to take care of displacements in the older industries."

Taking a long view, automation is likely to be accompanied by a progressive reduction of working hours. This should go a long way towards offsetting unemployment. Moreover, longer leisure would create new occupations and would accentuate the existing trend towards the relative expansion of service industries as distinct from goods industries. As automation tends to raise the standard of living, there would be an increased demand not only for goods whose prices have been reduced through automation, but for other kinds of goods as well, so that the industries producing them would employ additional labor. It is, perhaps, not unduly optimistic to hope that more leisure, together with the higher standard of living, will mean an increase in the demand for artists of every kind and for others catering to cultural requirements.

So long as postwar circumstances remain substantially unchanged, automation would be proceeding in an atmosphere of inflationary boom. Given an adequate degree of flexibility of labor, any employee who has become superfluous through automation should easily find some kind of new job. There would be a reversal of the postwar flow of labor from rural to urban districts, from nonproductive to directly productive occupations, from the household and from retirement to the factories. Automation would be accompanied by an increase in the prices of raw materials, so that mineworkers and agricultural laborers could be paid higher wages. It is true that farmers would not be able to outbid those manufacturers who benefit by automation, but workers who have become redundant in towns could pursue a tolerable existence by taking up farm labor.

There would be inevitably a certain amount of transitional unemployment. Pockets of unemployment might arise through automation in offices. But a reduction in the number of office workers through the use of computers and other automatic machinery for routine work would be a step in the right direction. There has been for some time an unmistakable trend towards the relative increase in the number of office workers. In the United States during the thirty years ended 1950 the number of factory workers increased by 53 per cent, that of office workers by 150 per cent. In Britain there has been a similar trend. In 1951 there were 2¼ million clerks. As Dr. Bowden observed at the Conference of the Institute of Management in 1955, Britain was becoming "a nation of clerks." A reversal of this trend, during a period when the redundant clerks could easily find alternative occupations, should not be regarded as a major tragedy from a national point of view, even if it is bound to cause inconvenience and hardship to many individuals.

In any case there is room for two opinions even about the effect of automation on office employment. The official American view is that it does not necessarily reduce the demand for clerical labor. Giving evidence before the Congressional Subcommittee, Mr. James P. Mitchell, U.S. Secretary of Labor, quoted the instance of an insurance company which, after installation of electronic data machines continued to face a clerical labor shortage, because of the ever-expanding volume of business. And Mr. Robert W. Burgess, Director of the Department of Commerce Bureau of the Census, stated that, on the basis of past experience, there is every reason to believe that the development of cheap and versatile electronic data-processing machines will not be accompanied by a major reduction, if any, in the number of office jobs. He believed that "the lower costs and increased possibilities for timely information have made it possible to meet more of the demand for increased facts to guide decisions by American businessmen and governments." Instead of causing unemployment among office workers, automation tends to increase the requirements of better service, which necessitates large office staffs side by side with electronic computers. Although it would be inadvisable to generalize about the validity of the conclusions reached by the two officials, their opinions should go some way toward counteracting the alarmist view that electronic computers will necessarily mean large-scale unemployment among clerical workers. In this respect too, as in other respects, a great deal depends on whether the economy remains expansionary or not.

Taking everything into consideration, it seems that fears

of technological unemployment are grossly exaggerated. To reduce these fears to absurdity, the National Association of Manufacturers pointed out in its evidence before the Congressional Committee that, if technological progress really resulted in unemployment, the United States would have in 1955 some 40 million unemployed, because it is now possible to produce goods with about two-fifths as much labor per unit as in 1910.

Those who recall the large-scale unemployment of the interwar period in support of their arguments against automation are guilty of the logical fallacy of arguing on the basis of false analogy. They should be reminded that unemployment during that period was not due to any noteworthy extent to technological progress. The slump in the early twenties was a reaction from the exaggerated post-armistice boom. Inadequacy of consumers' purchasing power, over-saving resulting from the unequal distribution of national incomes, and a restrictionist monetary policy, were the main causes of unemployment in various countries between the wars. The heavy unemployment in the United States during the thirties was brought about by the slump which resulted mainly from overspeculation.

The only technological cause of unemployment during the interwar period was the adoption of tractors and combines in agriculture. In addition to displacing some agricultural labor it led to an increase in output with no corresponding expansion in the purchasing power of the masses. But this mechanization occurred mainly during a period when the economic climate was distinctly deflationary so that it was bound to produce a deflationary effect.

Admittedly, even though automation does not cause large-scale technological unemployment during a period of inflationary expansion, it may produce deferred effects if and when, for no matter what reason, a deflationary trend should develop. Labor-saving equipment installed before the turn of the trend would then enable industrial firms to reduce the number of their employees without having to curtail their output too drastically. This problem will be dealt with in greater detail in Chapter 12 on business cycles. Here we shall confine ourselves to pointing out that the conclusion inferred from this argument is not to delay automation, because by doing so we are liable to incur unemployment through obsolescence, leading to deflation. The remedy is to proceed with automation at a reasonable pace as a means of eliminating one of the possible causes of deflation.

Apart from technological unemployment, automation may cause unemployment as a result of bottlenecks resulting from shortages of raw materials, electric power, or fuel. Should automation proceed at a very high rate, increased demand may cause such bottlenecks which may hold up production and would cause passing unemployment. There is even a possibility of a complete exhaustion of some irreplaceable raw materials, leading to unemployment of a more lasting character. This subject will be discussed in Chapter 15.

Hitherto we have been dealing with unemployment arising from a very rapid progress of automation. But unemployment is likely to arise also through inadequacy of such progress, if other producers at home or abroad proceed with automation at a higher rate; they may be able to undersell the less progressive producers, and the latter may then have to curtail their output and may even have to close down if they lose their markets. The cumulative effects of a large number of bankruptcies would be deflation and unemployment on a large scale.

It may well be asked why such a situation has not already arisen as a result of the uneven rate at which automation is proceeding in various countries, and within the same countries as between various firms. The explanation is that in an inflationary climate producers are not prepared to pass on to the consumer the benefits derived from automation. They do not cut their prices, for the time being, and the less progressive firms are thus given a chance to catch up with the more progressive firms. But sooner or later the latter might decide to cut their prices, and this would mean unemployment through obsolescence. The difference between technological unemployment created by automation and obsolescence unemployment created by inability to keep pace with the progress of automation is that obsolescence unemployment is more liable to be self-aggravating. Amidst an inflationary background technological unemployment is bound to be temporary and relatively moderate. For one thing, care is taken for social considerations, that the spending power of the victims of automation is not unduly reduced. If, however, a firm is compelled to dismiss its workers, not because they have become redundant through labor-saving equipment, but because it has lost its markets, it cannot afford to pay generous compensation, or retain them until they have found some other employment, or re-train them for other jobs.

If obsolescence unemployment is the result of price-cutting by automated foreign rivals, the effect of the losses incurred will become aggravated, from a national point of view, by the deterioration of the balance of payments. A nation which lags behind its commercial rivals in the sphere of automation is likely to have a perennial adverse balance of payments. This would mean a depletion of its gold reserve to such an extent that it would have to cut its imports of vital raw materials. Thus in addition to unemployment through obsolescence it would suffer also unemployment through bottlenecks, for even its automated firms might have to curtail their output through lack of imported raw materials. If the government tries to improve the balance of payments with the aid of a credit squeeze, it causes financial unemployment.

Financial unemployment may also result from automation if its progress is so rapid that the capital expenditure involved unduly accentuates an existing inflationary trend or if it is accompanied by excessive wage increases. In the absence of an adequate degree of saving, and of self-restraint by wage-earners, boards of directors and consumers, in the form of moderation of wage claims and dividends, inflation arising from automation may reach a stage at which it calls for credit squeezes leading to unemployment. The inflationary trend is not inherent in automation but is due to the weakness of human nature. Automation need not cause financial unemployment if the interests concerned can exercise a certain degree of self-denial for the sake of enabling automation to proceed unhampered by measures that governments are impelled to take in face of excessive inflation.

If technological unemployment, or any other kind of unemployment arising directly or indirectly from automation, were to assume such dimensions as to cause an appreciable decline in the national income, it would set in motion a deflationary spiral which would accentuate the extent of unemployment.

There is no reason why automation should lead to unemployment through change of demand, unless its progress in other countries should divert purchasing power towards imported goods, so that the loss to the firms affected by it would not be offset by the expansion of other firms within the country.

From the foregoing it appears that the problem of unemployment, as a direct or indirect consequence of automation, though not nearly as grave as is suggested by Dr. Wiener, is in fact not so negligible as it is claimed to be by enthusiasts of the new system. The gravest danger arises not through an unduly high rate of automation but through an unduly slow rate of automation. Those who are opposed to automation for fear of technological unemployment do not realize that if their policy were followed their country would be exposed to much more extensive and intractable non-technological unemployment.

Automation is bound to proceed sooner or later, whether we like it or not. Our choice does not rest between automation and full employment but between prompt automation with the possibility of moderate temporary unemployment and delayed automation with the certainty of grave perennial unemployment, until our progress has caught up with that of our competitors.

The only circumstance that is likely to mitigate the threat to those countries which have not proceeded with automation as fast as their rivals, is that during a period of expansion and inflation the more advanced firms are not likely to lower their prices unduly, if at all. Their desire to earn bigger profits, or to take the line of least resistance by yielding to wage demands, instead of lowering their prices in accordance with the reduction of their costs, may give the less advanced countries a breathing space during which they have a chance of catching up with the progress of their more dynamic rivals. But the first business recession would be accompanied by price cuts, and the backward firms would then feel the full weight of the disadvantages of being left behind in the "auto-mation race."

In his evidence before the Congressional Subcommittee, Diebold draws a distinction between the effect of automation on employment while it is in process of being established, and that when it has become a settled part of the economy. He believes that, since automation tends to increase the amount of capital per head of labor employed, once it is completed it will tend to reduce rather than increase the dismissal of employees. Their pay will represent a relatively small item in the expenditure of automated firms, compared with the charges on the increased fixed capital, so that it will not be worth while to dismiss them. Even though Mr. Diebold quotes with approval Keynes's flippant wisecrack that "in the long run we are all dead," he attaches, rightly, great importance to this essential difference between the short-run and long-run effect of automation.

CHAPTER EIGHT

EXPANDING PRODUCTION

EARLIER in this book we referred to the theory that inventions are liable to appear on the scene when they are needed. The recent spurt in the development of automation appears to confirm this theory. The inventions which made this progress possible certainly arrived when the world was ready for them from an economic, social, and political point of view. Automation gained prominence at a time when the need for increasing production became distinctly more urgent, and when the essentially expansionary character of the economy made its adoption considerably easier than it would have been during a period of contracting or stagnant economy.

It has, of course, always been one of the foremost aims of mankind to raise its standard of living. In the past, however, there was a tendency for an improvement in this sphere to be confined largely to a relatively narrow circle of beneficiaries. Until comparatively recently the standard of living of the large masses was progressing rather more slowly than that of the higher-income groups. It is only since the thirties that Jeremy Bentham's principle that we should aim at the highest degree of happiness for the largest number has in fact become the supreme end in practical politics. Benefit from progress is no longer the privilege of a small minority. The masses now claim and receive their share of it. This means, of course, that, while in the past a relatively small increase in production met the requirements of the rising standard of living, in the changed circumstances a very considerable increase in the output of goods and services is needed in order to raise the standard of living of the masses.

The reasons why it has become all-important in our days to increase production may be summarized as follows:

(1) All democratic countries have committed themselves, to a greater or less extent, to the Welfare State. The lower-income groups have been provided with social service benefits of various kinds. The financial burdens of social security tend to increase rapidly, and they can only be borne by the productive section of the community, without having to assume unduly heavy sacrifices, if the volume of production increases.

(2) The last few years have witnessed considerable progress towards equality of income, which will probably continue; or, at any rate, it is not likely to be reversed to any very large degree. A more equal distribution of wealth may mean equal misery or equal prosperity, according to whether or not the total of output available for distribution can be increased.

(3) There is a constant pressure on the economy by ever-increasing wage demands, chasing each other in a vicious spiral. Unless the volume of goods is also increased, the increase of consumers' purchasing power resulting from higher wages must mean nonstop inflation at an accelerating pace.

(4) For the first time in modern economic history an increase of production does not entail the threat of general overproduction. As a result of the more equal distribution of incomes through the increase in the incomes of the lower-

income groups, and the confiscatory taxation of higher incomes, the risk of oversaving has been practically removed. Say's Law, according to which all supply carries its own demand, having been denounced as hopelessly unreal during a generation which frequently experienced general overproduction through oversaving, has now become reality. Any increase in production tends to increase potential demand by increasing consumer incomes, thereby enabling consumers to buy the additional goods. The reason why Say's Law was unrealistic in the past was that the recipients of higher incomes were inclined from time to time to save an unduly large proportion of their incomes. With the scaling down of higher incomes that risk has now virtually ceased to exist.

(5) So far from there being a risk of inadequate spending of incomes, a strong trend has developed since the war toward the anticipation of future incomes through the expansion in the use of instalment credit. To satisfy the urgent and insistent demand arising from it, a greatly increased production in a large variety of consumer durable goods has become necessary.

(6) A drive to increase investment, both public and private, both productive and unproductive, has developed since the war. All nations have become increasingly conscious of the need for expanding their industrial and agricultural productive capacity. At the same time there is a growing demand for more and better roads, railways, schools, hospitals, etc. The expenditure involved in this drive competes with the increase in consumer demand and calls for increased production.

(7) Both capital goods and consumer durable goods have become incomparably more involved since pre-war days. A pre-war airliner, for instance, is like a toy model compared

with the giant postwar airliners which are not only much larger but are infinitely more elaborate, and the production of which requires many times more man-hours.

(8) The pre-war formula of "guns or butter" has been replaced by the formula of "guns *and* butter." Since the Korean conflict the democratic countries have realized the need for building up and maintaining considerable armed strength in the interest of their survival. They have also realized, however, that, should freedom from fear be achieved at the expense of freedom from want, the grave social and political consequences of a deterioration in the standard of living might wipe out the advantages of increased military strength. Any drastic curtailment of social services, or even any cessation of their further progress, might give rise to widespread discontent, providing an opportunity for Communism to fish in troubled waters. For this reason it is essential to increase output sufficiently to meet the combined military and civil claims on productive capacity.

(9) Another reason why increase in production has become a social and political necessity lies in the widespread realization that such an increase is now technologically practicable. Once the public has realized this, any regime which is unable or unwilling to take full advantage of these possibilities is liable to become utterly discredited.

(10) A number of new materials and manufactures have made their appearance since World War II. While many of them serve as substitutes for previously used goods, many others have created additional requirements. To satisfy them in addition to satisfying continuing need for the old goods, it is necessary to increase their total production.

(11) The production of synthetic materials made considerable progress during the war under the pressure of necessity.

This made us realize the need for developing the production of such materials in given circumstances, even if their production is costlier than that of the corresponding natural production. Apart from considerations of national defense, the synthetic production of certain key materials may become necessary also from the point of view of the balance of payments, or because of the possibility of shortages in the supplies of natural products. Automation, by tending to keep down the cost of production of synthetic materials, tends to facilitate the increase of their production.

(12) The world's population continues to expand, and in some backward countries the rate of expansion is likely to increase. In order to avoid a deterioration in the standard of living and to ensure its increase to a reasonable degree, the increase of production will have to outpace the increase of population.

(13) Almost for the first time the urgency of satisfying the needs of underdeveloped countries has come to be realized in the advanced countries. Hitherto the continued existence of many hundreds of millions of people at or below subsistence level was considered to be inevitable. During recent years a more humane conception has gained ground. At the same time the backward peoples themselves have become increasingly restless, developing violent nationalist or Communist tendencies. It is widely believed that an improvement in their living conditions would go a long way towards allaying this restlessness and preventing social and political upheavals.

The possibility of bringing about an expansion of production has also greatly increased simultaneously with the increase in the requirements for more goods. Apart from technological progress, the removal or reduction of financial obstacles to a major expansion of production played a vital part in preparing the way for automation.

The removal of this obstacle when the gold standard was suspended was the first step in the monetary sphere to prepare the way for an increase of production. An equally important change was the gradual adoption of a flexible credit policy under which the monetary authorities allowed a credit expansion to take place when the money was required for commercially and socially useful productive purposes.

A further change took place as a result of the institutional development of instalment credit referred to above. This placed the initiative in the hands of the consumer, who was enabled practically to dictate the pace at which production should be raised. It accentuated and even exaggerated the inflationary trend that is inherent in expanding production.

Automation can increase the output not only by increasing the productivity per man-hour but also by other means:

(1) By mitigating overfull employment, automation tends to discourage irresponsible strikes.

(2) In addition to the direct increase of the output in the industries immediately concerned, automation releases labor for other branches of production.

(3) Automation necessitates the production of new capital equipment which has to be replaced relatively frequently.

(4) The output of new industries which owe their existence to automation is often additional to the output of old industries.

(5) Increased production through automation calls for an increase in the production of raw materials.

(6) Automation entails a higher degree of standardization

and this, together with the lower cost per unit, tends to stimulate mass demand and mass production.

Admittedly, automation is not the only means by which to increase the output. The same end can be achieved by more intensive work, by longer working hours, by more efficient organization, by attracting labor from nonproductive occupations by enlisting the work of housewives, retired people and young people, by technological innovations outside the definition of automation, etc. Automation is, however, the most important means, with a very extensive scope for progress.

Automation can serve other ends than an increase in the production. Producers may prefer to use it for lowering costs. Employees may insist on its use for achieving shorter hours. Nevertheless, the possibility of using it to increase the output is there, and it is to the interest of all parties concerned that it should be used largely for that purpose. This is in fact for what it *is* used. It would be possible to quote a great many concrete instances of higher output through automation from the postwar experience of various industrial countries. Mr. Otto Pragan, giving evidence on behalf of the International Chemical Workers Union, before the Congressional Subcommittee, stated that during the eight years that followed the end of World War II the highly automated chemical industry in the United States increased its output by 53 per cent compared with an average increase of 25 per cent for all manufacturing industries. In a report by Professor Demyanyuk, read at the 1954 Conference of the Technical Sciences Section, Academy of Science of the U.S.S.R., it is stated that automation in the Soviet Union resulted in increases of between 40 and 200 per cent in the output of the motor-car, tractor, and ball-bearing industries. At the Institution of Production Engineers Conference at Margate in 1955, Mr. H. J. Graves, of Austin Motor Co., stated that the output of Austin Motors increased from 3,500 to 5,000 vehicles per week, mainly as a result of installing over sixty transfer machines and some 150 mechanisms of rotary-indexing types. Such instances could be multiplied.

It is of course difficult in most cases to ascertain to what exact extent the increase in the output is due to automation. But there can be no doubt that it results in a substantial direct increase, especially in an economy that is fully employed. In countries such as the United States, where the unemployed labor reserve has not been wholly exhausted, automation has contributed very substantially towards increasing output at the same time as increasing total employment.

If, under full employment, a firm wants to expand production, it has to entice workers from other firms by offering higher pay. This can be avoided by automation, thanks to which it is possible to increase the aggregate output, instead of one firm increasing its output at the expense of other producers, the total remaining unchanged. Indeed, as pointed out earlier, automation enables the dynamic industries to expand further, and at the same time to release manpower for the requirements of the static industries which became undermanned during the postwar years as a result of the demand for manpower by the dynamic industries.

In respect to the increase of the output through automation, as indeed in respect to other effects of automation on the national economy as a whole, it is well to bear in mind that at the present stage of the adoption of automatic methods, the producers affected represent a small minority of all producers, and even of all manufacturers. It is necessary to lay stress on this fact in order to be able to consider the effects of automation without losing our sense of proportion under the influence of some striking individual instances of increased productivity. Admittedly, there is scope for an even speedier progress than that witnessed in the United States since World War II. But on the whole it seems probable that, at any one time, or during a relatively brief period, the progress of automation will affect only a relatively small proportion of the national production.

CHAPTER NINE

DEFLATION OR INFLATION?

ALTHOUGH the effect of automation on the price level is one of the most important aspects of Automation Economics, it is probably the most neglected aspect of the subject. Some attention has been paid to the way in which the individual prices of the goods directly concerned are, or should be, affected; but very little has been written or said about the effect of automation on the trend of the general price level. Such reference as there has been to the subject appears to postulate that the average price level is determined by changes in individual prices. Since automation reduces the cost of production of individual manufactures, and creates the possibility of reducing their prices, it is generally assumed that it also tends to lower the average price level. In reality, although the basic assumption is an arithmetical truism, from an economic point of view the general price level is much more than a mere statistical average of individual prices. It is influenced by the trend of income and expenditure in general, by the volume of effective demand and its relation to the volume of goods and services, and by many other factors other than the cost of production. Individual prices, while determining the general price level, themselves depend to a large extent on the trend of the general price level.

The effect of automation even on the individual prices of the products of industries directly concerned is largely influenced by the trend of the general price level and of the economy. During a deflationary period, when the national economy is contracting, the full benefit of cuts in costs achieved through automation, or at any rate a large proportion of it, is likely to be passed on to the consumer in the form of lower prices. During an inflationary trend, on the other hand, when the national economy is expanding, a large part, if not the whole, of that benefit is liable to be retained by the producers in the form of higher profits and/or higher wages. Under postwar conditions the extent to which the trend of the price level is liable to affect the prices of goods produced by automated industries is much larger than the extent to which price-reduction-automated industries are liable to affect the average price level. It seems therefore logical to proceed with our analysis by ascertaining first how automation affects the general price level before we go into the question of its effect on individual prices.

The prevailing view is that automation tends to lower the price level, not only because it reduces the cost of production of goods per unit of output, but also because it increases the supply of goods. On the basis of the popular definition of inflation as "too much money chasing too few goods," any increase in the volume of goods should be expected to produce a disinflationary effect. This assumption that higher output should make for lower prices is correct—unless the increase in the volume of goods is accompanied by an increase in the volume of money. But that is precisely what is liable to happen when production is increased in circumstances involving an increase in the aggregate cost of production.

The importance of this aspect of the subject cannot be stressed sufficiently. It is the nightmare of many of those who have given some thought to Automation Economics that the world will suddenly be flooded with automatically-produced goods and that, owing to the fact that these goods are produced with the aid of a reduced labor force, there will not be enough purchasing power for the consumers to absorb them. These fears found perfect expression in Mr. Reuther's evidence before the Congressional Subcommittee. He said that when he inspected the highly automated plant of the Ford Motor Co. he was told by a high official of the firm, "Mr. Reuther, you are going to have trouble collecting union dues from all these machines." He replied, "You know, that is not bothering me. What is bothering me is that you are going to have more trouble selling them automobiles." What Mr. Reuther—whose evidence is in some other respects full of wisdom and common sense—appears to have overlooked is that, provided that the income of the nation *as a whole* continues to expand, even a complete automation of the motor industry would leave enough purchasing power in the hands of the consumer to absorb the increased output of motor cars. And we shall try to prove in this chapter that, so long as there is an increasing trend of the aggregate cost of production, it is liable to have an inherently inflationary effect on the national income and on the volume of purchasing power.

Leaving aside for the moment the special case of an increase in production through automation, let us examine the effect of increasing production in general on the price level. It is our contention that, provided that there is an increase in the *aggregate* cost of production, the increase in the output is likely to be preceded by an increase in prices, even if there is a decline in the cost per unit. This increase is in addition to the effect of the increased demand of manpower on wages and, through wages, on prices, that usually accompanies expanding production, especially under full employment.

This is a most important argument and has close bearing on the economic effects of automation. It deserves, therefore, detailed examination. The acceptance of our conclusion should go a long way towards allaying fears that automation tends necessarily to cause deflation, depression, and unemployment. It also disposes of the economic case for creating artificial consumer purchasing power in order to absorb the increased output resulting from automation.

It is generally agreed that, if an increase in production necessitates additional capital expenditure in the form of building and equipping factories, this tends to generate an inflationary effect. Materials are bought and wages are paid out in connection with the operation, so that more income is created without bringing about an immediate increase in the output of consumer goods. The volume of purchasing power is increased, but the volume of goods available for purchase will only be increased after the new factories have been completed and have been brought into production. Meanwhile more money is chasing an unchanged volume of goods.

What is apt to be overlooked is that an increase in the production of consumer goods tends to result in a similar effect even if it can be brought about through a more intensive use of the existing equipment without any additional capital expenditure. If a firm of motor manufacturers expands its production by increasing overtime, additional wages are paid out on every Friday, but the additional motor cars will not become available for some time. Meanwhile more money, in the form of additional income, will be chasing an unchanged volume of goods, in precisely the same way as in consequence of an expansion of plant, even though the time lag is not so long. The amounts involved in increased quantities of goods "in the pipeline" constitutes an addition to the working capital of the firms which increase their production. The effect is substantially the same as that of an addition to the fixed capital through building new factories.

Nor is this all. In order to increase production, manufacturers have to buy additional materials. If it is a "once for all" increase, the requirements may be covered out of inventory. If, however, there is a prolonged rising trend in production—as indeed there has been most of the time throughout many centuries, and more especially since the end of World War II—manufacturers have to increase their raw-material purchases. Producers of materials, in order to meet the additional demand, have to increase, in turn, their output. Unless and until this is done, the additional demand tends to raise raw-material prices. Markets in raw materials are usually very sensitive, and respond immediately even to a relatively moderate increase in demand. Long before the additional output of manufactures becomes available—indeed even before the additional raw-material purchases have actually reached the factories—there is likely to be an increase in the prices of the materials concerned, which affects not only the cost of the additionally produced manufactures but of all manufactures produced with the aid of those materials. This itself tends to create an inflationary climate, amidst which the additional incomes represented by the extra overtime earnings of factory workers will press on the price level.

What is more, any increase in the national income— whether it is due to additional capital expenditure, or to a budgetary deficit, or to increased consumer incomes through additional overtime pay—tends to produce a so-called "multiplier effect." It means that, when the recipients of the additional incomes spend their extra earnings, their surplus demand is liable to lead to an increase in the production of other goods. If employees of motor works spend their additional overtime pay on additional television sets, this leads to an increase in the production of television sets and to additional overtime pay to workers engaged in their production. The amount of additional income is thus spent and re-spent again and again, until the purchasing power it represents gradually disappears through saving, debt repayment, tax payment, etc. It means that the additional effective demand created by the injection of an additional income into the economy is apt to rise eventually to several times the figure of the original additional income.

It goes without saying that the time-lag effect and multiplier effect arising from an increase of the national income through increasing the aggregate cost of production can operate also in reverse. If the national income declines as a result of a reduction in the output, goods already in the pipeline will continue to appear for a time, so that the supply of goods will exceed the reduced purchasing power of consumers. The reduction of incomes will produce a multiplier effect, because those directly affected will reduce their purchases, and the decline of demand will induce producers of other goods to reduce their output, leading to further curtailment of incomes. Goods already in the pipeline continue to be completed, so that, when they become available, too many goods will be chasing a reduced volume of incomes.

Up to now we have been considering the effect of an increase of production in general, irrespective of its cause. Let us now examine how the situation is affected when the increase of production is due to automation. The answer depends on whether automation results in a reduction in the total amount spent on production by the community as a whole, as well as in the amount spent on a unit of product by the automated firms, or whether, owing to the increase in the aggregate volume of production or to the increase of wages, the aggregate cost of production for the entire community increases in spite of the cut in the cost per unit of goods produced by automated factories. In so far as the grand total paid out, for raw materials, transport, wages, etc., is reduced, it results in a reduction in total income and consumer purchasing power and should therefore tend to produce a deflationary effect. If, however, the total is increased, then the effect of automation will be inflationary even if the cost of production per unit is reduced; and—paradoxical as it may sound—even if part of the benefit of the lower cost is passed on to the consumer in the form of lower prices. For, during the "pipeline lag" described above, the volume of consumer purchasing power will increase without being accompanied by a corresponding increase in the volume of goods available to consumers.

Even if the goods produced through automation can eventually be offered at cheaper prices and in larger quantities, they will not become available till later. Meanwhile an increased volume of purchasing power is brought to bear on an unchanged total volume of goods, whether produced through automation or not. Moreover, even if, at the end of the pipeline-lag period, the prices of goods produced through automation are reduced, this only releases more purchasing power to buy more of those goods or of other goods. Given a previous increase in national income, a cut in the prices of some goods—unless it should cause widespread bankruptcy among non-automated firms—merely means that more money will be available to spend on those goods or on other goods.

It may be argued that, if it were practicable to achieve within a brief period a very high degree of automation throughout industry, aggregate money incomes might conceivably fall as a result of large-scale technological unemployment to such an extent that, when the additional goods produced by the automated factories become available, a large part of them would become unsalable in the absence of very drastic price cuts. Such a rapid and widespread automation seems, however, to be highly improbable. And in any case, an increase in the rate of automation would involve heavy capital expenditure. It is only after the accelerated progress of automation is completed that the increased spending on fixed capital is exceeded by a decline of spending on working capital. Even then, any reductions in the aggregate cost of production of automated industries would be easily absorbed in a general increasing trend of the national income.

It is true that that part of the proceeds of goods which represents profits is held back until some time after their sale. On the other hand, the multiplier effect of that part of the price of goods which is paid out before the goods become available creates additional incomes. Moreover, if the rising trend of production is continuous and involves a continuous rise in aggregate cost of production, then the income created today to pay for the cost of goods that will not become available until tomorrow should be more than enough to pay for the goods whose production was initiated yesterday and was completed today.

Once the rising trend in production comes to a halt, the volume of goods may catch up with the increase in the amount of income, after the multiplier has produced its full effect. If in the meantime the inflationary effect of the pipe-line lag has resulted in a rise in prices, then consumers may be unable to buy the whole of the additional goods in the absence of a further rise in their incomes. A stabilization in the volume of production may therefore be succeeded by a downward reaction in the trend of prices. If, however, the rise in production is continuous, then the volume of goods is unable to catch up with the increase in incomes, and the inflationary effect of rising production remains uninter-rupted. Against this background, employees are inclined to put forward and press wage demands, and employers are inclined to concede them, because they in turn are in a position to pass the additional cost on to the consumer, who again is both able and willing to pay the higher price.

The above outline of the effects of pipeline lags is neces-sarily oversimplified. What is essential is to realize that, apart altogether from the inflationary effect of re-equipping indus-try, there is also the additional inflationary effect of increasing output with the aid of the new equipment, always provided that the total current cost of production of the entire industry and the aggregate income of the community are higher than before.

In connection with this important proviso it is necessary to bear in mind the circumstances in which automation is being adopted. The three basic facts of the situation are the strong bargaining power of industrial employees, the expanding trend of the economy, and the inflationary atmos-phere.

Under large-scale unemployment, when the bargaining power of the labor unions is weak, industrial firms would be in a position to adopt automation for the purpose of cutting costs by dismissing the men who are replaced by machines. In postwar conditions, however, the unions in Britain, and to a large extent in the United States, are in a position to prevent large-scale redundancy dismissals. If employers want to introduce labor-saving machinery, they have to do so in a way which obviates the need for dismissing the men displaced by machines. They are at liberty to proceed with automation for the purpose of increasing their output, but they are likely to encounter resistance if they proceed with it for the purpose of reducing their staff. Given the existing balance of power between employers and employees, it is in many instances practically impossible to adopt automation in circumstances that would mean a decline in the aggregate cost of production of the firms or industries concerned. In any case, owing to the expanding trend and inflationary undertone of the economy as a whole, there is every inducement for employers to increase their output to an extent that involves an increase in the aggregate cost of production, in spite of the reduction of the cost of the unit through automation.

This is in fact what has happened in the overwhelming majority of instances both in Britain and in the United States. The evidence given before the Congressional Subcommittee on Automation contains a very large number of examples showing that automated industries, so far from reducing the number of their employees, actually increase them. Moreover, since a large proportion of their employees are upgraded, automation in prevailing circumstances tends to increase incomes rather than reduce them. It is true that union leaders, when giving evidence, quoted a number of instances in which automation was followed by reductions in the number of employees. The fact that both in the United

States and in Britain automation was accompanied by an increase in total employment and in national income shows, however, that in existing circumstances the danger of deflation through automation is not serious.

There is yet another reason why automation, if adopted in an expanding economy, does not bring about deflation. In deflationary conditions the progressive firms would use automation for price cuts. As we pointed out before, in inflationary conditions the dynamic firms prefer to maintain their prices or reduce them only slightly. Whether this is a good thing or a bad thing is irrelevant from the point of view with which we are concerned in the present chapter. What matters is that automation in such circumstances does not initiate a deflationary spiral. It seems that automation, like an increase of taxation, tends to exaggerate deflation during deflationary periods and inflation during inflationary periods.

Even if the prices of manufactures produced by automated industries are cut, it does not necessarily mean a fall in the average price level. For so long as the increased demand for raw materials tends to cause a rise in the prices of such materials, this is liable to offset the fall in the prices of manufactures produced by the recently automated firms. Any increase in the prices of materials has a very widespread effect on the price structure, while a decline in the price of some manufactures may not affect the cost-of-living index perceptibly. It ought also to be borne in mind that if the increase in industrial production is in response to a previously increased demand—which has been the case with motor cars, television sets, etc., during the fifties—it is not likely to cause any reduction in prices. Moreover, price-maintenance arrangements operate in respect to a very wide range of manufactures, and this may for a long time prevent the reduction of their prices in spite of the increase in the output.

There can of course be no doubt that, other things being equal, automation reduces the extent of inflation caused by expanding production. The point is largely academic, because without automation production is not likely to increase to the same extent. But, given an equal degree of expansion, its effect on prices is bound to be more moderate if it is achieved through automation, resulting in an increased productivity per man-hour, than if it is achieved by attracting workers from other occupations, or by working more overtime. Moreover, automation tends to mitigate to some extent the inflationary effect of the "pipeline lag," described earlier in this chapter, by reducing the time required for the process of production.

The proof of the pudding is in its eating. Those who are inclined to doubt the validity of the contention that, in the balance, automation is more likely to accentuate inflation than reverse it, should be reminded that during the forties and fifties automation was proceeding at a relatively high rate in the United States and in spite of this it was accompanied by a slowly rising trend of prices, apart from the temporary setbacks in 1949 and 1953-1954. One of the reasons why the rise was not nearly so pronounced as in Britain was that the rate of automation was much higher in the United States. The main effect of automation on the price level there was a mitigation of its rise.

During an inflationary period automation is disinflationary in a relative sense, in that the rise in the manufactures produced by automated factories does not keep pace with the general rising trend. All that mechanization in general and automation in particular seems to have done is to slow down to some extent the secular rise in prices. Between 1913 and 1955 the average hourly earnings of factory employees in the United States increased by 746 per cent, while the average prices of manufactures increased by 132 per cent only. The difference is largely accounted for by technological progress, but for which the rise in prices might have been much nearer 746 per cent than 132 per cent.

CHAPTER TEN

THE WAGES-PROFITS-PRICES TRIANGLE

THE way in which the benefits of automation are shared between employers, employees, and consumers is apt to influence considerably the effects of automation on price levels, consumer demand, saving, employment, the supply of risk capital, and the economic trend in general. It also tends to influence, directly and indirectly, the progress of automation itself. The allocation of benefits is of considerable importance also from a social point of view. It deserves, therefore, careful examination. This is one of the economic aspects of automation which has, in fact, received a great deal of attention. It has been considered, however, for the most part from a social or commercial rather than an economic point of view.

The conflicting claims of employers, employees, and consumers have been subject to heated controversy in which each interested party has been accusing the other of trying to secure an unduly large share of the benefits derived from automation. In reality it is simply the continuation of the age-old controversy. Both sides of industry press the claims which they have always pressed, long before automation was even thought of. They merely seek to reinforce their respective cases for an increased share in the proceeds of production with the aid of new arguments derived from their re-spective interpretations of the economic aspects of automation.

Spokesmen of labor insist that the amount saved with the aid of automatic methods should be allocated between em-ployees and consumers. In addition to higher wages and lower prices, they claim shorter hours, and a complete immunity from redundancy dismissals or its consequences. Spokesmen of industry argue that there must be no government inter-ference with the freedom of business firms to proceed with automation as they please, and that the benefits derived from it should be used largely for a reduction of the taxation of company profits and of high personal incomes.

Labor unions put forward with the utmost emphasis the claim that workers are entitled to the lion's share of any benefit derived from technological progress. Labor's claim to the full benefits of higher productivity is based on the as-sumption that all goods owe their existence exclusively to the exertions of the physical laborers directly engaged in their production. The emotional appeal of this claim has lately been reinforced by an economic argument about the need for increasing consumer purchasing power to enable them to buy the additional output resulting from automation. This argument has already been touched upon in the last chapter, where we pointed out that there is no need to worry about the possibility of a deficiency of purchasing power so long as the economy as a whole continues to expand.

Unless and until there is a setback in business activity and a declining trend in prices, wage demands resulting from automation can only be supported by considerations of social justice and of the need for maintaining good industrial relations. From the point of view of the former it must be remembered that, compared with pre-war conditions, there has already been a very far-reaching re-allocation of the proceeds of industrial production after the war for the benefit of labor.

To a large degree this is as it should be. But labor's claim that it is entitled to the full benefit from any increase in productivity resulting from automation is surely untenable. Apart from individual instances in which the workers suggested technical improvements, labor has not contributed towards the progress of automation. Indeed in many instances it has done its best to prevent or delay its progress.

Labor's claim for a share in increased productivity rests on the fact that automation does in fact increase to some degree the risk of unemployment. But, as we sought to prove in Chapter 7, the risk of unemployment is higher if a firm is left behind in the automation race than if it proceeds with automation at full speed. Even so, it is understandable if labor claims compensation for the uncertainty of employment created by action taken by employers, as distinct from the less easily recognizable uncertainty arising from absence of action. Although the claim is open to argument, it is better founded than the claim based on the need for increasing consumer purchasing power or on labor's share in increased productivity. There is everything to be said for meeting the claim to a reasonable degree for the sake of achieving better industrial relations.

It is arguable that higher wages are essential in order to encourage further progress of automation. As was already pointed out in Chapters 2, 3, and 5, cheap labor handicaps automation while high wages stimulate it. In the experience of a firm engaged in producing steam boilers, while at the end of World War II it was worth while to spend $25,000 on labor-saving equipment if it reduced labor requirements by one worker, today it is worth while to spend twice as much, owing to the higher cost of labor that is to be replaced by the machine. We must guard ourselves, however, from generalizing in this respect. Rising wages affect not only the cost of running the automated factory but also the cost of producing the new equipment. In instances where that cost, too, doubled during the interval, the higher wage level does not encourage automation. Moreover, any advantages derived from higher wages from the point of view of stimulating automation are liable to be offset, and more than offset, by the disadvantages of excessive wage increases indicated above.

On the face of it, the claim that the benefit of automation should go to the consumer may appear convincing. Apart from social considerations, from a purely economic point of view this would ensure automatically the absorption of the increased output. On closer examination it seems, however, that the situation is not nearly so simple. We saw in the last chapter that the result of any drastic price cuts through automation is liable to drive less efficient firms into bankruptcy. Let us imagine, for the sake of argument, that all firms decided to cut their prices to the full extent of the reduction of their costs through automation. The result would be a sweeping wave of bankruptcies. Many firms, without having to close down, would feel impelled to cut their production. There would be an immediate increase of obsolescence unemployment, at a moment when, owing to the progress of automation, the progressive firms would not require additional labor.

It is impossible to estimate the probable extent of the repercussions of such unemployment on the economic trend. If the price cuts were confined to British industries, the relatively slow rate of automation in Britain would limit the effect. But it is, to say the least, conceivable that in some internationally competitive industries any drastic British price cuts would be followed by price cuts in the United States and in other industrial countries. This might force many more British firms out of business. Moreover, any large-scale price cuts in the United States might lead to large-scale obsolescence unemployment in this country also. Owing to the predominant position the United States occupies in world economy, this might initiate a deflationary spiral on an international scale.

From a point of view of equity there is, of course, everything to be said for the utmost degree of price reductions, so that the largest possible number of people should be able to enjoy the benefits of progress.

Shareholders too are entitled to a portion of the benefit derived from automation. After all, it was their money that acquired the modern equipment. From an economic point of view it is essential to encourage risk capital for new ventures, especially having regard to the additional capital requirements resulting from automation, and to the increased rate of obsolescence resulting from the accelerated rate of technological progress. Encouragement must be given through reasonable dividend increases.

The extent to which higher wages and higher dividends are economically justified depends on the prevailing trend of prices and of demand. During an inflationary period there is a strong case for setting aside the greater part of the benefit derived from automation in the form of blocked credits which would be released to wage-earners and shareholders as and when a declining trend developed in prices and in demand. Some such solution would be to the interests of employees and shareholders alike. It would moderate inflation and would go some way towards preventing a recession from developing into a slump. If workers were to agree that their share of the benefits of automation should be paid into trust funds—which could be organized on the lines of the trust funds set up by the American automobile industry under the Guaranteed Annual Wage Agreements of 1955— instead of receiving cash increases, this would have a considerable stabilizing effect. The same principle would have to be applied, however, to some extent to dividends, in order that the formula should be acceptable to workers.

Another point to be considered is the allocation of profits from automation between dividends, liquid reserves, and additional capital expenditure. Any unduly rigid limitation of dividends would have the disadvantage, from the point of view of the progress of automation, of encouraging take-over bids, owing to the low Stock Exchange quotation of the shares. The chances are that the financiers who gained control of industrial firms by such means would not be interested in any long-term plans of capital expenditure but would aim at a quick profit on capital appreciation, or would raid the liquid reserves to finance their other ventures. They would not be likely to immobilize the reserves of the firm by engaging in further automation.

An advantage of dividend increases, from the point of view of automation, is that they increase the resources available for risk capital. On the other hand, too large dividend increases would be contrary to the interests of automation. They would deplete the resources available to the firms for further automation or for the replacement of their existing automatic equipment by even more up-to-date equipment.

Yet another claimant for a share in the benefits of automation is the government. Under existing conditions of taxation, its share, in the form of taxes on company profits and on higher personal incomes, is very considerable. A reduction of such taxes is advocated both in Britain and in the United States as a means of encouraging automation.

Beyond doubt the allocation of automation benefits presents some very difficult problems. It is possible to make out a strong case for or against any of the one-sided solutions advocated by the interests concerned. What is needed is to find some intelligent compromise in which all legitimate interests would be reconciled with each other and with the public interest. This end must be approached through a realization of the great advantages of the correct solution from the point of view of the progress of automation, and of the disadvantages of any one-sided solution. The blocking of at least part of the higher wages and dividends received as a result of automation might be the answer to the problem.

CHAPTER ELEVEN

CAPITAL REQUIREMENTS

IN EXAMINING the question of capital requirements arising from automation we have to differentiate between fixed capital, consisting of investment in fixed assets, and working capital, consisting of goods in process. The effect of automation on the requirements of the two types of capital is totally different. Requirements of fixed capital arising from automation are by far the more important. Expert opinion is sharply divided on the question whether automation is likely to increase or reduce such requirements. There can be, of course, no two opinions about its effect on initial requirements during the transitional period while existing equipment is replaced. Provided that the rate at which the replacement takes place exceeds the normal rate of obsolescence, automation necessarily means an increase in initial capital investment. The rate of automation is an all-important factor.

Capital requirements arising from automation vary from industry to industry. Some types of the new equipment are distinctly cheaper than the old equipment they have to replace, while in other instances they are much more expensive. It is impossible to generalize, and it is entirely a matter of guesswork whether, in the main, capital requirements increase or decrease if automation is proceeding at a moderate rate.

If a firm is not handicapped in its automation plans by

the existence of an obsolete factory, it may be able to achieve considerable economies by building an automated factory. As it requires fewer workers per unit of output, it requires relatively smaller buildings and a smaller site, and less has to be spent on devices ensuring the safety and hygiene of the workers, and on canteens and other welfare institutions. If, owing to the smallness of the shifts, it is possible to work two or three shifts a day, so that the machinery is used more intensively, less machinery is required, so that factories can be altogether much smaller. If the total number of employees, including office workers and repair and maintenance men, is small, there is no need for the factory to be located near a large town, and the cost of the site is lower per square foot.

On the other hand, the automatic processes involved necessitate a high degree of precision, and for this reason, among others, machinery is apt to be costlier. Owing to its more intensive use, and also to its highly complicated character, more frequent replacements are likely to be needed.

Above all, the rate of obsolescence is likely to be high because of the accelerated pace at which better equipment is invented and produced. M. A. Hollengreen, President of the American Machine Tool Builders Association, is quoted as having said in September 1955, "Advances in machine tools have never been as rapid as they have been in the past five years, and most members of the industry expect the pace to be stepped up considerably in the next half decade." And D. J. Davis, giving evidence before the Congressional Committee on behalf of the Ford Motor Company, said, "If a machine-tool manufacturer comes out with something better than he did last year, and it saves us money, your competitor is going to buy it up if you don't." Much automatic equipment is likely to be scrapped long before it has come to an end of its useful life, to be replaced by even better equipment that saves even more labor, time and materials, or achieves an even higher degree of precision. This consideration alone seems to indicate an increase in the permanent rate of capital requirements resulting from automation.

Another all-important consideration making for high capital requirements is that in conditions of boom and inflation, automation is more likely to be adopted for the sake of increasing the output than for the sake of reducing the number of employees. For this reason the observations made earlier in this chapter on economies resulting from the smaller number of workers employed may only be valid in a relative sense, in comparison with the volume of the output. Even if capital requirements per unit of output are reduced, the absolute amount of capital requirements may have to be maintained and possibly even increased.

In the United States as elsewhere, the chemical industry is one of the most highly automated industries. Otto Pragan, giving evidence before the Congressional Subcommittee on behalf of the International Chemical Workers Union, said that in 1954 the average amount spent on new equipment by the chemical industry was $2,240 per production worker, compared with the average of $877 for manufacturing industry as a whole. In that year the total capital equipment was $12,933 per production worker for the entire manufacturing industry. The average for the ammonia industry, in which automation has reached a particularly advanced stage, was $42,500.

A substantial reduction of capital requirements may conceivably arise if automation of factories producing automatic equipment and mass production of such equipment affects its cost. From this point of view it is important to note the recent progress of automation in the electronics industry in the United States, which until comparatively recently produced its equipment largely by non-automatic methods. On the other hand, the production of transfer machines to ensure continuous flow of production requires a variety of individual designs and is not expected to become automated to any large degree.

It seems reasonable to assume that in the course of time the cost of automatic equipment will be reduced, and with it will decline the amount of capital requirements. While many inventions aim at saving current expenses with the aid of larger initial capital investment, many other inventions aim at reducing the cost of these capital investments per unit of output. No doubt in due course progress will be made toward that end. This will not mean, however, a decline in the absolute amount of capital requirements. The larger output may necessitate bigger investment in spite of the decline per unit.

According to statistical evidence, there is a distinct trend towards a reduction in the value of fixed assets in comparison with the value of the annual output. It cannot be taken for granted, however, that this trend is bound to continue. Much depends on the nature of future inventions. It stands to reason that the progressive replacement of man by machine means more capital requirements and not less.

Whether or not automation brings a reduction in absolute or relative requirements of fixed capital, it usually brings a reduction in the amount of working capital per unit of output. In most instances it is adopted primarily for the purpose of reducing the cost of production, which means that the same amount of output calls for less working capital. Another way in which this end is achieved by automation is by speeding up the process of production. Not only is there less work-ing capital required per unit of output but it is required for a shorter period.

On the other hand if automation is adopted, not for the purpose of reducing costs but for the purpose of increasing output, and if the extent of this increase is such as to result in an increase in the aggregate cost, then there may not be any reduction in the requirements of working capital. It depends on whether or not the larger requirements resulting from the higher output are offset by the reduction of the period for which the working capital is required. It must be borne in mind, however, that working capital includes also the amounts invested in inventories, and these are likely to increase as a result of expanding production through auto-mation. We saw in Chapter 9 that the increase of the output resulting from automation is liable to cause an increase in the prices of materials. Also during periods of rising pro-duction and rising prices industrial firms are inclined to keep larger stocks of materials. These considerations point toward increased requirements of working capital. Nevertheless it seems conceivable that in the balance requirements of work-ing capital may decline, or at any rate their increase will be much smaller than the reduction of the requirements of fixed capital.

The next step is to consider the way in which any addi-tional capital requirements arising from automation are covered. In Communist countries this problem is relatively simple. Under a totalitarian regime it is possible to force the workers to work very hard on a very low standard of living. The proportion of the output reserved for investment can thus be increased, by simply reducing or keeping down the production of consumer goods. This explains the spectacular

rate at which Soviet Russia has been proceeding with industrialization in general and with automation in particular.
All that the Soviet Government needs to do is to keep down
the production of consumer goods and employ a high proportion of the country's productive capacity for the production of capital assets. The rate at which factories are erected
in the Soviet Union necessarily means the continuation of
housing conditions compared with which the worst-over-
crowded slums in the West are almost luxurious. And the
rate at which the factories are equipped necessarily means
chronic shortage of manufactures for consumers.

Democratic countries can only inflict comparable hardships on the masses of consumers during wars, when there is
a high degree of willingness to make sacrifices in the interests
of national survival. It is difficult in time of peace to persuade
the public that it is to their interests in the long run to reduce
their present standard of living for the sake of expanding
producing capacity and thereby to ensure an increase in
their future standard of living. The "in the long run we are
all dead" mentality cannot be overcome without controls.
And any large-scale effort to divert production capacity from
consumer goods to capital goods with the aid of controls is
bound to encounter a stiffening resistance if it goes beyond a
certain stage. In most democratic countries wartime allo-
cations of materials, labor and other facilities practically
disappeared by the middle fifties. Governments have relin-
quished their wartime power to refuse building licenses for
factories which are to produce goods with a low priority, for
the sake of diverting investment towards the production of
capital goods and of other goods with a high priority. It is
now left largely to the investors and the financial institutions
to take their choice between various types of schemes for

industrial expansion, whether in the form of automation or other forms.

Governments have considerable powers to encourage or discourage the flow of financial resources to privately owned industries engaged in automation. This can be done by monetary and fiscal devices. The official monetary policy can influence, to a high degree, the volume of capital resources available for the subscriptions to new issues, and for the willingness of investors to subscribe. Its influence on the willingness and ability of banks to provide temporary accommodation pending the issue of loans, and to finance any increased requirements of working capital resulting from an increase in the aggregate cost of production through automation in an expanding economy, is even more direct and decisive. Fiscal devices in the form of tax concessions to industry largely determine the ability and willingness of industrial firms to retain part of their profits and to use it for capital investment.

There is also the device of unofficial dividend restraint which is, however, a double-edged weapon. While it may increase the amount of undistributed profits available for investment, it tends to discourage subscriptions to new share capital issues for financing automation projects of new firms or of firms with inadequate reserves. A further device at the government's disposal is the encouragement of lending to industrial firms by officially sponsored finance companies. Moreover selective credit control could go a long way towards diverting credit resources towards the requirements of additional working capital arising from automation. This aspect will be examined in greater detail in Chapter 13, dealing with monetary policy.

The availability of capital for the requirements of automation depends to a very large degree on the extent of the pressure of unions for higher wages. To say that the more money is paid out in wages the less is available for investment in automation would grossly oversimplify the situation. It would suggest that the total amount of resources is rigidly fixed, so that any addition to wages would have to be deducted from the resources available for enterprise. This is not so under our present flexible system. The burden of higher wages can be passed on to the consumer in the form of higher prices. But fundamentally this oversimplified formula represents, nevertheless, the truth. For excessive wage increases, through their inflationary effects, are likely to compel the authorities sooner or later to restrict credit, as a result of which the supply of capital funds available for financing automation is reduced.

It is often alleged that during the inter-war period expansion of production was held up by "tight-fisted bankers" who were unwilling to provide the financial resources needed by industry. During most of the time since World War II, however, they have been quite willing to expand credit to finance an expansion of production, whether it was to be achieved by automation or by other means. The role which was attributed to them between the wars has now been assumed by the unions. In Britain it was their excessive wage demands that forced the government to resort to credit squeezes, to the detriment of the progress of automation. This simple fact is not realized sufficiently. When in 1955-1956 inflation in Great Britain was gathering speed, the increase in capital expenditure—by the government, by nationalized industries, and by private enterprise—was blamed for it. Yet the rate of capital investment in Britain remained considerably lower than in the United States and some other countries, where inflation did not proceed at nearly as high a rate as in Britain. The difference in the degree to which investment resulted in inflation may be attributed to the stronger pressure for higher wages, and to the higher degree of equalitarianism in Britain, as a result of which consumer incomes were increased beyond the extent of the increase in the output, and a smaller proportion of the increased incomes was saved.

An increase in the propensity to save would assist in the provision of capital reserves needed for ensuring the increase of automation in various ways. Additional savings would increase the financial resources available for that purpose. The disinflationary effect of an increase in savings would obviate the necessity for the authorities to apply credit squeezes from time to time for the sake of moderating an inflationary trend. The same effect would be produced as a result of the improvement of the balance of payments resulting from a lower domestic demand for goods. And the reduction of consumer demand would mean lower requirements of working capital, which would leave more resources for meeting the requirements of fixed capital for automation.

We saw in the last chapter that the way in which the benefits derived from automation are shared between capital, labor, and the consumer, and the way in which capital's share is divided between the enterprise and its shareholders, may affect the volume of capital resources in general, and of risk capital in particular, that is available for automation. They influence not only the amounts available but also the willingness of firms and investors to use their funds for the requirements of automation.

In his article in *Harper's Magazine,* quoted in Chapter 4, Drucker lays considerable stress on the steadiness of capital expenditure arising from automation. He points out that once a firm has embarked upon such capital expenditure it has to carry on in spite of any business recession; otherwise the capital already invested would be wasted. According to Drucker, this explains why the business recessions of 1951 and 1954 in the United States were not accentuated by unduly sharp declines in capital expenditure. Beyond doubt there is a great deal in this argument. Admittedly, automation was not the sole reason of the steadier flow of capital expenditure in the United States during the postwar period. The assumption that the Government is wedded to the policy of high employment created an optimistic outlook, leading managements to be willing to proceed with their capital expenditure plans, even if immediate prospects did not appear to be promising. They felt they could afford to take a longer view. But the nature of investment in connection with automation must have also contributed towards the steadying of the flow of investment.

CHAPTER TWELVE

ARE BUSINESS CYCLES DEAD?

ARE business cycles a matter of past history, or are they an ever-present menace? The answer to this question is a matter of utmost importance from the point of view of automation. We saw in the earlier chapters that it makes all the difference to the effects of automation whether it is adopted during a boom or during a depression. If automation makes progress during a boom it brings larger output amidst stable full employment. If it is applied during a depression it brings a fall of prices and a decline of employment. And there is a possibility that automation achieved during a period of boom may have delayed adverse effect during a subsequent slump or depression.

Since the war the world has experienced no slumps comparable with those which occurred at fairly frequent intervals before the war. During a relatively prolonged period we have had no cyclic crises in the accepted sense of the term. In spite of this, there are at least as many people who think that a slump is just round the corner as there are who think that we have finished with business cycles forever. Expert opinion, too, is divided between those who feel that the periodically recurrent major slumps have now been replaced by more frequent minor recessions, such as have been witnessed in the United States in 1949 and 1953, and those who believe that nothing has changed fundamentally. Indeed some economists even feel that we are now more vulnerable than before the war. The pessimists suspect each minor recession of being a possible opening phase of a major slump. In between these recessions they worry themselves over the boom on the ground that growing prosperity and rising prices makes the economy increasingly vulnerable. They strongly disagree with the "prosperity forever" attitude of the optimists and recall that the same things were said during the "nonstop" prosperity of the twenties.

For studying the prospects of automation it is necessary to be able to form an idea which of these diametrically opposite views is nearer the truth. Another question that calls for an answer is whether the present degree of automation has itself reduced or increased the risk of a slump, and whether its further progress is likely to reduce or increase it. Furthermore, there is the question of how automation would affect the course of a slump or a depression, if one should arise for no matter what reason. Finally, it should be interesting to examine how a slump or a depression would affect the progress of automation. In order to answer these questions, it is necessary to summarize briefly some of the most widely accepted explanations of business cycles such as operated before the war, and to form an opinion whether the various causes to which various crises were rightly or wrongly attributed are still in operation.

Classical economists were inclined to ignore the business cycle, or at any rate to regard any deviation from "normal" conditions as a purely temporary state of affairs which would be adjusted automatically in the absence of artificial interference with the free working of the competitive system and the price mechanism. Artificial interferences with free competition and with the free play of prices, by monopolies, rigidities of the economy, or government controls, are—according to the classical theory—the causes of any abnormal dislocation that may develop, the readjustment of which may at times be a painful process. The extent of such interference with a free play of economic forces increased considerably during World War II, and even now it is probably above its pre-war level in most countries in spite of the progress in the liberalization of the economies in the democratic world. Notwithstanding this, in the existing situation no crises need arise from the dislocations created by artificially maintained economic conditions, because amidst an expanding economy most adjustments which take place eventually assume the form of further rises in prices which are absorbed in the general stream of inflation. Indeed, as we shall try to show below, one of the sources of the danger of a setback in trade lies not in excessive control but in excessive freedom which now gives an even wider scope for errors of judgment than before World War II.

According to the psychological explanation of business cycles, the ups and downs of the economy are due to alternative waves of optimism and pessimism on the part of entrepreneurs, bankers, merchants, investors, speculators, and consumers. Confidence in everlasting prosperity is bound to exaggerate demand, leading to expansion of production, expansion of credit, promotions of mushroom firms, accumulation of large inventories, increase of consumption, and an orgy of speculation. Conversely, a wave of distrust discourages producers, merchants, bankers, consumers, and speculators alike. From the latter point of view the situation has become distinctly better than it was before the war, precisely because of the absence of cyclic slumps during the postwar period. It is true, as we pointed out above, that even in the

United States, amidst the unprecedented prosperity prevailing there, there are many people who live in constant fear of a slump. There are many others, however, who are convinced that, owing to the changed conditions and policies and owing to our better monetary technique, the danger of a major slump is now very remote.

On the basis of this assumption, which is held widely in American business circles, and also because automation requires long-term investment plans, capital expenditure in the United States is now based on long-term plans instead of being influenced by the ups and downs of the immediate situation. As we observed in the last chapter, dealing with capital requirements, one of the reasons why postwar business recessions in the United States have been moderate is precisely that they do not generate a sufficient degree of pessimism to lead to wholesale suspension of capital expenditure. The American Telegraph and Telephone Co., for instance, announced that it had a large-term program of development, which was not affected by the vicissitudes of boom and recession.

It is well worth noting, however, that whenever the boom appears to be proceeding too fast, fears of a major slump become more general and widespread. The volume of consumer demand is liable to fluctuate more widely than before the war. This is partly due to the increase in the level of incomes, giving more consumers the free choice between saving or spending part of their incomes, instead of having to live to the limit of their incomes in order to satisfy their essential requirements. In addition, the expansion of the use of instalment credits has provided consumers with the option of living far beyond their present means by mortgaging their future earnings. The combined effect of these changes is that the range within which the propensity to consume is liable to change has become much wider.

Another pre-war theory attributes cyclic slumps to the cumulative effects of the coincidence of errors of judgment by a number of individual firms or industries. Apart altogether from the possibility of miscalculating the general trend, there is a possibility of miscalculating the capacity of the market of absorbing one particular product or group of products. The result of such errors of judgment is the building-up of excessive producing capacity, and the accumulation of excessive inventories, leading eventually to painful liquidations, the curtailment of production, failures involving financial losses, and unemployment in the industries affected. If such errors of judgment are committed by a few firms only, or by comparatively unimportant isolated industries, their effect on the general economy may be moderate. If, however, they are committed by some vitally important industry, or by a number of industries, the resulting fall in incomes and losses through bankruptcies might initiate a slump through their cumulative effect. As Reuther aptly remarked, "Nothing breeds unemployment like unemployment." Isolated pockets of unemployment might easily merge into general unemployment.

From this point of view our economy is, if anything, even more vulnerable than it was before the war, owing to our higher standard of living. Discretionary incomes—that part of taxed incomes which is not required for essentials—have increased. There is now a much wider choice between various kinds of goods on which the consumers may, if they wish, spend their incomes. It is therefore even more difficult to foresee future demand for any particular type of goods than before World War II. Changes of taste may produce much stronger effects on individual industries. The higher the standard of living rises above subsistence level the larger proportion of consumer income is spent on luxuries and the less predictable the direction of its spending is liable to become.

If in spite of this the post-war period experienced no major slumps through the cumulative effects of miscalculations, it is largely because of the prevailing inflationary trend. Owing to the ever-increasing volume of consumer purchasing power and the almost uninterrupted rise in prices, practically everything that is produced nowadays can be sold sooner or later. Usually the difference between correct and erroneous forecasting of consumer tastes merely affects the size of profits earned, and the slower or faster rate of turnover in the goods.

A theory which has become very popular is the theory of inventory cycles. According to this, a prolonged period of prosperity is usually accompanied by the accumulation of increased inventories by wholesale merchants and retailers, in order to meet the growing demand, and to benefit by the rising trend of prices. There is always a possibility of over-estimating the extent of future demand, or that at a certain stage, the merchants arrive at the conclusion that their inventories are excessive. The result is a reduction or suspension of orders by merchants. As goods continue to emerge from the pipeline, manufacturers involuntarily accumulate excessive inventories. Sooner or later they decide to curtail their output. This leads to a gradual liquidation of inventories, first by the merchants and then by the manufacturers.

There have been several such inventory cycles in the United States since the war. Their extent was not unduly large. But automation is likely to exaggerate inventory cycles because it is difficult to alter production schedules of automated factories, so that output is likely to run at a high level for some time, in spite of the accumulation of excessive inventories.

The monetary theory of business cycles explains the alternation of booms and slumps on the grounds of excessive credit expansions, which have to be halted or reversed sooner or later owing to the fact that the volume of credit reaches the limit set to it by statutory or traditional reserve requirements or by the prudence or timidity of bankers. During a period of restrictionist monetary policy the monetary factor was indeed all-important as a cause of slumps. Under the gold standard the amount of the gold reserve largely determined the limits of credit expansion, and the banks had to conform to these limits by refusing new credits when that limit was approached. Even before the limit was actually reached there was a tendency for interest rates to rise, a tendency that was often reinforced by official action aimed at discouraging further credit expansion. The result was forced liquidations of stocks leading to a fall in prices, curtailment of production, unemployment, and fall in consumer purchasing power. When the volume of credit had thus been reduced, bankers were once more willing to lend, and a period of business expansion followed.

As a result of the suspension of the gold standard, and even more of the adoption of a more flexible monetary system, the monetary cause of business cycles is today not nearly so important as it was before the war. Its importance varies, however, according to the gold resources and balance-of-payments position of a country. In the United States it is relatively unimportant, owing to the favorable balance-of-payments position and the large gold reserve that is sufficient to meet any conceivable trade deficit. In Britain the monetary factor is expected to assume considerable importance from time to time, because of the inadequate gold reserve and unsatisfactory balance-of-payments position. When as a result of rapid expansion of domestic consumption the British balance of payments turns adverse, the government tries to correct it by means of monetary restrictions, which tend to cause a setback in production and consumption. This is what happened in 1952 and again in 1955-1956. The main difference between the pre-war and postwar situation from this point of view is that before the war monetary influences on the business trend were largely automatic, while at present they are due to deliberate measures of monetary policy.

Even though the United States need not worry about the gold reserve or the balance of payments, the possibility of a recession through monetary causes cannot be ruled out. It might arise whenever the authorities feel impelled to take drastic disinflationary measures in order to correct a boom which threatens to get out of control. Of course the aim is merely to mop up inflation. But there is always a risk of disinflation developing into deflation.

A variety of underconsumption theories of business cycles found widespread support before World War II. According to these theories slumps were due to deficiency of consumer purchasing power that was liable to develop from time to time. Underconsumption theories can be divided into three groups, according to whether they attribute cyclic crises to maldistribution of incomes, to oversaving, or to deflationary time lags. Ever since Karl Marx it has been suggested by many writers that, since a large part of the proceeds of production is retained by a small number of wealthy people, the remainder of the proceeds is not sufficient to buy up all the goods which have been produced, as the volume of consumption by rich people does not increase in proportion to their incomes. This theory overlooks the fact that considerable incomes are created in connection with the production of capital goods, which does not increase, or does not immediately increase, the volume of goods available to consumers. In any case, since the war, the extent of maldistribution of incomes has been reduced considerably in all democratic countries. Even if the argument had been valid before the war it is certainly no longer applicable in postwar conditions.

A more refined version of the pre-war underconsumption theory allows for the fact that part of the proceeds of production consists of capital goods and is not immediately available to consumers. On the other hand, it emphasizes that recipients of income are liable to save too high a proportion of their incomes and that this may lead from time to time to a deficiency of demand. According to the Keynesian principle, all is well so long as intended savings do not exceed the amounts spent on capital goods. But if there is an excess of intended saving over intended investment, the result is a depression, because the amount spent does not buy the entire volume of goods produced. Keynes believed that the tendency towards oversaving was inherent in the economic system and that the propensity to save tended to increase with increasing incomes. In situations such as developed after the war, however, it seems that saving, so far from being excessive, is often distinctly deficient. It may not adequately cover the amounts spent on investment. This is one of the explanations of the inflationary undertone of the postwar economy. Indeed, as is shown by the expansion of instalment credits to which we referred above, there is now a strong tendency towards anticipating future incomes rather than accumulating past incomes. Postwar prosperity is not menaced by underconsumption either through maldistribution of income or through oversaving.

A third version of the underconsumption theory assumes the existence of various deflationary time lags. Prominent among them is the time lag between the earning and distribution of business profits. According to this theory, an increase in business activities is liable to become reversed automatically, because expanding business means expanding profits, and the delayed distribution of larger profits tends to immobilize a large amount of purchasing power. This time lag, and other deflationary time lags, received a great deal of attention. On the other hand, the existence of an inflationary time lag inherent in expanding production has been ignored almost completely by economists. Yet it seems reasonable to assume that, together with the multiplier effect generated by expanding production it heavily outweighs the combined effects of all deflationary time lags. In any case, since the ratio of profits to wages has declined compared with the inter-war period, even if the theory had been valid before the war the importance of this factor has since declined materially.

There remains to consider the explanation of cyclical crises on the basis of overinvestment. According to this theory, if the rate at which capital expands is excessive, a stage is liable to be reached sooner or later at which productive capacity will exceed purchasing power. This theory has been put forward in various forms ever since Marx. Its most widely accepted version, put forward by Schumpeter, attributes crises to the fact that technological innovations usually appear in clusters, followed by sterile periods during which little new investment occurs, while the markets are flooded with goods produced as a result of the application of the earlier innovations.

What these theories appear to overlook is that, when a factory is completed it cannot flood the community with additional goods without first creating additional purchasing power as a result of paying out additional wages, buying more raw materials, etc., long before the goods appear on the market. Whether or not the overinvestment theory was correct before the war, there can be no doubt that, owing to postwar conditions of wage-inflation and Welfare State-spending, the danger of a deficiency of purchasing power compared with total producing capacity is remote.

It seems that in the balance the risk of a slump is less pronounced since World War II than it was before the war. Apart from the wider distribution of incomes, and the existence of "creeping inflation" which seems to be able to prevent periodic slumps, there are now also a number of built-in stabilizers in the system which did not exist before the war. The development of social-service benefits provides a countercyclical device. The high level of taxation too is counter-cyclical in a sense, because a fall in the national income automatically creates a large government deficit. In Britain moreover, the government has a trump card which it can play when there is a decline in demand. The repayment of Post-War Credits would increase consumer purchasing power by some £500 million, and would create a considerable immediate addition to consumer demand. The government was wise in resisting popular clamor for an accelerated repayment of Post-War Credits during the period of inflationary boom. Indeed it would be wise to build up much larger amounts of similar countercyclical reserves in the form of "post-boom credits."

The United States is practically the only country whose postwar experience may give some indication of the change in respect to business cycles. As Robertson pointed out at a Conference of the International Economic Association on the business cycle in the postwar world, held at Oxford in 1952, "Britain's post-war history is not in terms of any recognisable cyclical pattern but in terms of a biannually recurrent oscillation between exchange panic and fool's paradise." The postwar economic history of many other countries was the chronicle of more or less advanced and continuous inflation amidst which cyclical trends had but little scope. Sweden and some other smaller countries provided a better test. But because of their smallness they were largely dependent on international trends, and "imported" booms and recessions influenced the situation. In the United States alone, the "new economics" could be observed at work to a reasonable degree. It seems that changed conditions, coupled with intelligent monetary policy, have succeeded here in keeping booms and depressions within reasonable bounds for a period of over ten years. While it would be premature to regard this experience as conclusive, it justifies guarded hopes that the business cycle in the pre-war sense has been brought under control. It is widely believed, however, that freedom from slumps can only be achieved by maintaining the continuity of expansion at the cost of a mild nonstop inflation.

This long digression was necessary because, as we pointed out above, the prospects of automation are closely linked with those of the maintenance of the present conditions. Our next step is to examine how the progress of automation itself is likely to affect the prospects of a recurrence of business cycles.

Notwithstanding opinions to the contrary, automation tends to stimulate booms, so long as its pace remains relatively moderate. Amidst conditions prevailing in the postwar world it is likely to lead to increased profits, which again tends to stimulate investment. Given the high level of employment, the expanding trend of the economy, and the inflationary atmosphere, pockets of technological unemployment arising from automation will not be able to reverse the trend. But the situation is not without dangers. Buckingham said in his evidence before the Congressional Subcommittee, "As automation advances in our basic industries, the American economy becomes like a rocket which must continue to accelerate or else fall from the sky." So long as additional investment in fixed capital through the progress of automation exceeds any reductions in working capital resulting from accomplished automation, the "rocket" continues to accelerate.

Drucker claims that automation exerts a stabilizing influence on the economy by its steadying effect on the flow of the output. "Automation requires continuous production at a set level of output for a considerable period of time—three months, six months, maybe a year. This means that short-time adjustments cannot normally be taken care of by changing production schedules except at exorbitant cost." From the point of view of business cycles, this additional rigidity introduced in the economy can cut both ways. Drucker may be right about its stabilizing influence against relatively moderate pressure making for a depression. If inventory cycles do not materially increase unemployment, quite possibly the deficiency of demand that is the cause of excessive inventories may pass without doing much harm. But in face of a major disequilibrium making for a major depression, the effect of automation in delaying the adjustment of the output to a fall in demand is liable to aggravate the slump, if and when it does take place.

In a non-automated economy a setback in demand is met

by a reduction in the supply through a curtailment of the output. Equilibrium is thus restored, and recovery may set in from the lower level. To the extent to which automation produces the effect attributed to it by Drucker, any lasting setback in demand is liable to lead to a substantial increase in inventories. It tends to prolong thereby the downward course of inventory cycles. There can be no recovery until the surplus stocks have been more or less liquidated. To that end, prices may have to decline much more than in a non-automated economy. This means a sharper slump, or a more prolonged depression. The importance of this factor is likely to grow with the progress of automation.

It is true, automation may moderate the decline in demand, because automated industries, once their automation is completed, are not likely to resort to wholesale dismissals of their reduced staffs, consisting mostly of trained specialists, and because investment plans in automatic equipment, once initiated, cannot be interrupted without losing the amount already spent. But so long as the highly automated section of industry does not represent the major part of productive capacity, this stabilizing effect will be outweighed by the influences affecting the non-automated part of the economy. In that case the effect of the maintenance of a higher output by automated industries on inventories may aggravate, in the main, the setback in business activity. It seems therefore that, while Drucker's diagnosis is correct, his prognosis may prove to be wrong in the event of a prolonged depression.

Changes in expectations can produce magnified effects. Should recession fears become widespread, they might produce a psychological effect in the form of a setback not justified by the material effects of automation. Dr. Wiener's alarmist prophecy, that automation will cause a slump overshadowing that of the thirties, might go some way towards providing its own justification if it should convert a large number of people to defeatism. So the psychological effect of automation depends entirely on our own attitude. Those who hold and propagate defeatist views incur grave responsibility. The right attitude is to regard the prospects with realism, but not to yield to defeatism which has no justification in the known facts of the situation or in a well-balanced assessment of the prospects.

Another way in which automation is liable to increase the risk of slump is by its effect on firms and industries which are unable or unwilling to keep pace with their more progressive rivals. Wholesale bankruptcies, or even drastic curtailments of production, by a large number of firms would initiate a depression.

Automation is not likely to initiate a slump through its monetary effects. The chances are that it will strengthen the expansionary bias of monetary policy rather than contribute toward restoring a limit to credit expansion. For it is very tempting to argue in favor of financing automation even at the cost of moderate inflation, having regard to its long-term effect on the standard of living. On the other hand, an increase of production achieved through automation is less inflationary than increase of production achieved through means involving a bigger increase in the aggregate cost of production, always provided that the rate of automation is not so high as to involve very large additional capital expenditure. Indirectly, however, automation may lead to an accentuation of the inflationary trend. The evidence of higher productivity, and especially of higher profits resulting from automation, may encourage excessive wage demands, and the inflationary effect of the wage spiral may lead to drastic disinflationary action involving the risk of initiating a deflationary spiral.

It may be asked whether automation is likely to increase to some degree the risk of underconsumption through maldistribution of incomes. For it is likely to cause an increase in profits, and it is likely to widen wage differentials in favor of skilled labor. But the chances are that, under prevailing taxation, relatively little of the taxed profits will be saved, and a large proportion of what is saved will be re-invested. As for wage differentials, we have pointed out above that experience since the war has shown that an increase in incomes, so far from leading to an increase in the propensity to save, is apt to increase the propensity to dissave in the form of additional instalment commitments.

There remains the question of the effect of automation on overinvestment. Beyond doubt it will necessitate an increase in the total value of capital assets. But technological progress, so far from being accompanied by a decline in the yield of capital as predicted by Keynes, tends to increase profits. This should increase the propensity to save.

The idea that because automation means increased investment it increases the likelihood of a slump through a reaction to overinvestment is entirely untenable. Automation has opened up an almost unlimited possibility of demand for capital goods. Even after the system has achieved maturity—which stage is not likely to be reached for a long time—there will be a continuous need for replacement on such a scale that it should keep the capital-goods industry busy even in the complete absence of new investment. Admittedly, in so far as automation tends to increase the relative proportion of capital-goods output, any setback in trade is liable to create an exaggerated effect.

Although fears that automation is liable to lead to slump through overinvestment are unfounded, there can be no doubt that, if deflation should develop through no matter what causes, automation would greatly exaggerate any downward trend in purchasing power, prices and employment. Just as under inflationary conditions it strengthens the influences making for a boom, under deflationary conditions it would be used for reducing the number of employees.

Once a slump has started, the installation of new equipment is likely to be suspended after the end of the transitional period during which equipment ordered before the slump would continue to arrive. Even replacement might be drastically curtailed. But once the slump is followed by chronic depression, automation would resume its course, almost entirely with the object of reducing cost of production.

This chapter has admittedly barely touched the surface of the problems arising from the impact of automation on business cycles. Volumes could and should be written on that subject. What has been said above should be sufficient, however, to cast doubt on the widely held belief that automation necessarily means slump because progress can only be achieved at the cost of instability. That rule is valid in a different sense. Expanding production, whether through automation or through other means, almost inevitably causes inflation. But even from this point of view, other things being equal, automation tends to moderate the extent of inflation, and, in given circumstances, it may even eliminate it altogether.

There is, at any rate, one way in which automation is able to make an important direct contribution towards mitigating the danger of a slump. It enables both businessmen and government officials to secure more up-to-date information with which they are able to plan their policies on the basis of a better knowledge of the situation regarding production, stocks, sales, etc. At present much of the relevant vitally important statistical material is so hopelessly in arrears that by the time the government becomes aware of what is happening the trend may have gathered too much momentum to be easily checked. And business executives may have missed the right moment to take or reverse decisions. By being better informed the government and businessmen would be able to act more promptly and more effectively. Although this would not necessarily safeguard them from errors of judgment, on the basis of better and more up-to-date information they will stand a better chance of making correct decisions.

CHAPTER THIRTEEN

MONETARY POLICY
IN THE AUTOMATIC AGE

THE object of this chapter is to examine how automation is likely to affect monetary policy, and how monetary policy is likely to affect automation. We saw in the last chapter that the Government's task of preventing or mitigating business cycles has now become even more important than before, because although automation does not initiate cyclic crises it is liable to exaggerate them. The question is to what extent the desired end can be attained with the aid of monetary-policy devices.

During the twenties monetary policy was regarded by many economists as an almost all-powerful means with which it was considered possible to regulate booms and slumps provided that the application of its devices is not "too late and too little." As a result of the experience of the thirties, however, the prestige of monetary policy declined, because it proved itself helpless in face of the persistent depression. During the war too, in the prevailing artificial conditions, monetary policy remained well in the background. It was not until the early fifties that monetary policy came to be "rediscovered." Its revived prestige proved to be, however, of short duration. By the middle fifties the conclusion was reached, at any rate in Britain, that, when overfull employment generates an inflationary wage spiral, the time-honored devices of monetary policy are almost as helpless as they were twenty years earlier in the face of a chronic depression.

Automation is capable of affecting monetary policy to the extent to which the progressive adoption and operation of automatic equipment strengthens or weakens the prevailing economic trend. In so far as it tends to mitigate the inflationary trend it facilitates the task of the authorities. This result is achieved in the following way:

(1) Automation tends to mitigate the extent of overfull employment.

(2) It enables producers to lower their prices, or at any rate to refrain from raising them.

(3) It increases the volume of goods available to consumers.

(4) It shortens the time required for manufacturing, and thereby reduces the working capital per unit.

(5) It tends to reverse, or at any rate moderate, the equalitarian trend.

On the other hand, automation tends to increase the difficulties of the monetary authorities in the following ways:

(1) It tends to increase investment in fixed capital, at any rate, during the transition period.

(2) Increased industrial production tends to increase the prices of raw materials.

(3) The rigidity of production schedules of automated firms tends to reduce the effect of disinflationary measures on inventories.

This latter point was touched upon in the previous chapter, in connection with the effect of automation on business cycles. It means that, if the monetary authorities wish to correct an unwanted increase in inventories, they are unable to make adequate headway with automated industries which are likely to uphold their production schedules in spite of high interest rates and credit squeezes, and in spite of a decline in purchasing power and demand. For this reason the disinflationary measures will have to bear more heavily on the non-automated section of the industry in order to make up for the immunity of the automated section. Moreover during a period of deflation the automated industries are in a better position to reduce their prices, thereby contributing towards the downward trend, at a time when the official policy aims at checking or mitigating it. On the other hand, as pointed out before, capital expenditure in connection with automation is less likely to be cut as a result of a business recession than other industrial investment. In this respect automation tends to make the task of the monetary authorities easier.

In the main, it is safe to say that automation may facilitate the task of the monetary authorities in resisting inflation, but it increases their difficulties in face of deflation. In particular, automation may assist the authorities in regaining control over the monetary trend during an inflationary period by mitigating the maladjustment of the balance of power between employers and employees, thereby checking or slowing down the irresistible inflationary wage spiral against which monetary devices are helpless. If the balance of power is readjusted as a result of automation, monetary policy stands a chance of coming into its own once more.

The extent to which an inflationary wage spiral generated by overfull employment is immune to the effects of monetary devices is not realized sufficiently. High interest rates cannot discourage borrowing if, as a result of the wage spiral, the rise in prices largely reduces the real rate of interest paid by debtors who repay their loans in depreciated currency. What is even less widely realized is that, in face of a wage spiral, even a credit squeeze can produce no direct effect, because wage increases are self-financing. If a firm wants to increase its *output* with the aid of its existing equipment, by increasing employment, it has to obtain additional credit facilities to finance the additional goods in the pipeline. If, on the other hand, it agrees to raise *wages,* there is no need as a rule to secure additional credit, because in an inflationary climate it is in a position to add the increased wages immediately to the prices of its goods. There is no time lag involved, and no increase of the working capital is called for. This means that, while curtailment of bank credits may be effective in preventing an expansion of production, it is not directly effective in preventing wage increases. Indirectly the effect of reversing the expansion of production through credit cuts may react on wages as and when it causes a reduction in the extent of overfull employment. To the extent to which automation tends to mitigate overfull employment, it reduces the need for cutting production to fight inflation with the aid of credit squeezes.

Automation tends to increase the difficulties of the monetary authorities in counteracting a depression once it has developed. In itself automation will not produce a slump. On the contrary, by mitigating inflation it obviates the need for drastic disinflationary monetary measures which carry the risk of provoking a slump. But, once a slump has developed for other reasons, it is liable to become exaggerated as a result of large-scale reductions in the number of employees, and of drastic price cuts, made possible by automation, achieved before the slump. It is true that the automated works are likely to continue to operate for some time on the basis of their original production schedule. But if the installation of automatic equipment had been accompanied by the adoption of "feather-bedding" arrangements, the change in the balance of power resulting from the turn of the trend would be likely to induce managements to carry out the long-deferred dismissal of the redundant workers. Moreover, during a period of depression firms possessing adequate financial reserves may decide to proceed with automation for the purpose of cutting their costs, which will aggravate the depression once expenditure on fixed assets is completed.

During a future depression there will be greater possibility of substantial price cuts, owing to cuts in costs achieved with the aid of automation. This will make the task of the authorities to resist a decline of prices even more difficult than it was during the pre-automation period. Firms which had reached an advanced stage of automation during a boom, but which did not then pass on to the consumer the benefits of automation in the form of reduced prices, would now be well able to do so during a slump and during a prolonged depression. Amidst a deflationary atmosphere their action would drive less efficient producers out of business and the forced liquidation of their bankrupt stocks would accentuate the deflationary spiral. In face of this trend the conventional devices of monetary policy would be utterly helpless, except possibly to the extent to which holders of stocks of unsalable goods would be prepared to carry them because of cheap and plentiful credit facilities.

The realization of this effect of automation should induce the monetary authorities to reverse their disinflationary policies the moment there appears to be the slightest risk of the development of a deflationary spiral. They must try to err on the safe side. The risk of a recession degenerating into a deflationary slump has increased as a result of automation. The more advanced the stage that automation has reached the more important it becomes for the authorities to keep their monetary policy finely balanced between inflation and deflation, and the more important it will become to avoid erring on the side of deflation.

Even in the absence of automation most governments are, not unnaturally, more anxious to prevent a slump than to prevent a boom. Since it is practically impossible to keep exactly to a happy medium, the authorities prefer to put up with moderate inflation rather than risk a grave recession through exaggerated disinflationary measures. Because automation is liable to aggravate the consequences of a depression, its progress is likely to induce the authorities to be even more inclined to err on the inflationary side.

This is not the only way in which automation tends to influence monetary policy in favor of inflation. Should the pace of its progress become accentuated, the increase in capital investment would produce a strongly inflationary effect. It might more than offset the mitigation of inflation resulting from the reduction of overfull employment by accomplished automation. The authorities will find it increasingly difficult to resist pressure for more credit if it is needed for accelerating the pace of automation, as and when public opinion becomes increasingly automation-conscious. In view of the paramount importance of keeping pace with our business rivals and potential enemies, any attempt to starve industry of funds needed for automation would expose the authorities to strong and well-deserved criticism. Indeed, owing to the urgency and importance of the progress of automation, the view will gain ground that if that progress can only be achieved at the cost of an accentuation of inflation, that price is well worth paying. The authorities are likely to be urged to provide all the funds needed for automation and to pursue a monetary policy enabling private interests to raise the necessary capital. They may be inclined to heed warnings about the highly detrimental effect that automation is liable to produce if it is delayed during a boom, and has to be adopted during a deflationary period, as a means of survival in face of ruthless price-cutting by more progressive rivals. Automation is certainly a game which should be played from strength, not from weakness. One of the ways to ensure this is to secure the continuity of economic expansion with the aid of monetary expansion during the period of progress in automation.

To reconcile the conflicting needs of encouraging automation and yet of preventing an accentuation of inflation, it has become very important for the authorities to stimulate an increase in saving. In the circumstances it might be worth while to consider the possibility of the issue of securities with guaranteed purchasing power for the benefit of small savers. Another unconventional device, which Macmillan adopted in Britain in 1956, is lottery loans, through which the gambling instincts of the public would be turned into constructive use.

Resistance to the wage spiral is the alternative to a substantial increase of savings, as a means of mitigating the inflationary results of a speedy progress of automation. To that end it might become necessary from time to time to break the spiral by means of a credit squeeze or high bank rate, even if it meant a temporary setback in the progress of automation. This could be avoided if the workers and their unions could be persuaded that, in the interests of the development of automation it is essential that they should moderate their claims, at any rate until those claims could be satisfied without causing inflation, out of increased productivity.

In order to get the maximum of benefit from automation

it is important to avoid, as far as possible, interference with the continuity of the flow of demand for both consumer goods and capital goods. This aspect of automation economics was made plain by Drucker in his article in *Harper's Magazine*. He stressed the importance of a steady market to absorb the steady flow of goods produced by automated industries.

If disinflationary monetary measures were to interrupt the continuous flow of demand at frequent intervals, it would be bound to be detrimental both to the progress of automation and to the results of automation already achieved. For this reason the case for nonmonetary measures may gain in strength in given circumstances. At any rate those responsible for shaping economic policy, and those who criticize their decisions, should be aware of the argument and should resist the ever-present temptation to be guided exclusively or extensively by their ideological dogmatism for or against controls.

What was said above indicated not only the way automation is liable to affect monetary policy but to some extent the way monetary policy is liable to affect automation. As we have pointed out earlier, in a general way, the change in the basic principles of monetary policy in our lifetime has been very helpful to the progress of automation. But for the suspension of the gold standard and the adoption of a flexible credit policy, automation could not have made much progress.

Once automation has been carried out, the increased production by automated factories is not hampered unduly by an increase in interest rates. Thanks to lower costs, there should be a sufficiently wide profit margin on the current output to absorb the additional interest charges. But progress of automation is liable to be hampered by an increase in the cost of the capital investment involved. When a firm has to decide whether it would be worth its while to replace human labor by machine, it has to compare the saving in wages with the additional interest charges on the necessary funds. This means that low interest rates tend to encourage automation while high interest rates tend to discourage it by making borderline cases unprofitable.

What matters from the point of view of automation is not so much the cost of loans but their sufficiency. As far as big firms are concerned, they are able to overcome the effect of credit restriction on the capital market by financing automation with the aid of non-banking loans. The supply of such loans is, to some extent at any rate, independent of the influence of the authorities. Big firms which have facilities for borrowing outside the banks, pending the issue of shares or debentures, are in a position to do so because they can afford to pay attractive interest rates. On the other hand, the adoption of automation by small firms depends on monetary policy to a much higher degree. In view of the important part small firms can play in pioneering new automation devices, it is essential that monetary policy should not be such as to make automation the exclusive privilege of the big firms. Alternatively, the government should provide special facilities to firms willing to proceed with automation but hampered by lack of funds.

If it is necessary to set a ceiling to monetary facilities to industry, monetary policy should aim at giving a priority to automation in preference to investment that would merely expand producing capacity without materially reducing the cost per unit. Selective credit control should be applied in such a way as to encourage automation.

CHAPTER FOURTEEN

BALANCE-OF-PAYMENTS PROBLEMS

BEFORE World War II, limitations of financial resources under a restrictive monetary system prevented mankind from making full use of technological progress for an increase in the standard of living. We saw in the last chapter that this obstacle has now been largely overcome, if not removed altogether, by the most advanced countries. In spite of this, some of these countries are not in a position to make full use of their increased productive capacity. Even if there are no longer financial limitations in the form of a deliberate restrictionist monetary policy, balance-of-payments difficulties necessitate the re-imposition of monetary restrictions from time to time. Production cannot be raised in accordance with the immense possibilities created by technological progress, unless the country concerned can increase its exports sufficiently to pay for the larger imports resulting from the expansion of production. Larger output means more imports of raw materials; and larger national income means increased consumption both of imported goods and of goods that would otherwise be available for export.

Even if a government were prepared to encourage rapid automation in spite of the inflationary effect of the capital expenditure involved, a deficit in the balance of payments would call a halt to this progress from time to time. It is only countries such as the United States, which is fortunate enough to possess a large gold reserve or a persistently favorable balance of payments, that are able to expand their output with impunity over a long period. For countries such as Britain the problem of the balance of payments is of first-rate importance from the point of view of its bearing on automation.

Once a high degree of automation is achieved, it tends to assist in the creation of a favorable balance of payments, especially if it involves a decline in the aggregate cost of production, and at the same time the output increases. Lower aggregate cost of production would mean a decline in the volume of domestic consumer demand. Less would be spent on imports of consumer goods and a larger surplus would be available for exports. The export of a large proportion of the increased output would be assisted by the reduction in the cost per unit of goods brought about by automation. It is true that if output is increased it means larger imports of raw material even in the absence of an increase in the aggregate cost of production. There is a good chance, however, that, owing to the effect of automation on output and costs, this would be more than offset by an increase of exports.

The result is different when automation is carried out in circumstances which cause an increase in the aggregate cost of production in spite of the decline in the cost per unit—which is, in fact, what has been happening during recent years. It means an increase in imports, and, even though the reduction in the cost per unit creates the possibility of a corresponding increase in exports, it is by no means certain that producers will take full advantage of this possibility. Owing to boom-like conditions in the home market, they might find it easier to dispose of their output at home instead of relinquishing part of the profits achieved through automation by cutting their prices in order to increase their exports in the face of keen foreign competition. However, the possibility of an export drive exists, thanks to the reduction in the cost per unit.

Automation tends to affect the balance of payments as a result of inevitable discrepancies between the degree of its progress in various countries. If the rate of automation is higher in other industrial countries, a country's balance of payments may suffer in consequence. Much depends on the circumstances in which the progress of automation is achieved by one's rivals. If it is achieved in an inflationary atmosphere, producers may not be prepared to reduce their prices for the purpose of expanding their export any more than they are prepared to reduce them to boost their sales in the home market. In that case the exporters of the more progressive countries will make bigger profits but will not increase their exports, so that the balance-of-payments position will remain unchanged. The possibility of making use of the reduction in the cost to launch an export drive would exist, however. It would lead to price-cutting as soon as the home market in the progressive country ceased to be able to absorb the increased output. This would expose the less progressive country to the possibility of a sharp deterioration in the balance of payments.

To the extent to which such a deterioration leads to unemployment at home it would tend to correct automatically the balance of payments through a reduction in imports and an increase in the exportable surplus of goods unaffected by the increased foreign competition. If, however, the less progressive country is experiencing inflationary conditions, then the lost export markets are offset by an expansion of sales in the domestic market. This is often the case nowadays, in view of the determination of government, Parliament and public opinion to maintain full employment at all costs. On more than one occasion during the postwar period in Britain, in order to counteract the development of pockets of unemployment through the loss of export markets the remedy used was the artificial stimulation of domestic consumption. The process was aptly denounced as amounting to an attempt to lift up ourselves by our bootlaces. Nevertheless, since the basic principle of the new fetish-worship that has replaced the worship of the golden calf under the gold standard is that full employment must be maintained at all costs, it was considered admissible.

Notwithstanding the pursuit of such a policy, the development of large-scale unemployment through balance-of-payments difficulties for a country lagging behind in automation is only a question of time. Sooner or later the gold reserve will become depleted, and it will then become necessary to cut imports of raw materials or to adopt ruthless disinflationary measures.

Automation need not be confined to industrial countries. Its application in raw-material-producing countries is liable to aggravate the balance-of-payments difficulties of industrial countries, even if the rate of progress in the former countries is slower. It means that a larger proportion of their domestic requirements is met out of the increased domestic production. If the advantages of cuts in costs through automation are combined with the advantages of cheap labor, underdeveloped countries may become the rivals of industrial countries in the sphere of international trade. They may even penetrate into the domestic markets of industrial countries. At the same time, however, experience shows that industrialization of underdeveloped countries is apt to increase not only their capacity to export but also their propensity to import. While our exporters may lose certain markets, they are able to find other markets in goods of higher quality, which consumers of the developing backward countries can now afford to buy as a result of the increase of their incomes.

If we are left behind in the international automation race it does not affect the exporting capacity of our industries which are not suitable for automation. For instance, the automation of the American ready-made clothing industry would not affect the export trade of Savile Row. But domestic demand for luxuries may be affected by the general deterioration of business conditions resulting from unemployment through obsolescence.

One of the ways in which advances in automation may affect foreign trade is through creating new requirements in capital goods. Countries which lead the way are likely to establish themselves in the markets for automatic equipment abroad. The advantages of being first in the field are important, because of the high requirements of replacement units for automatic equipment.

In so far as automation leads to a more intensive utilization of machinery through working two or three shifts, it will affect the balance of payments favorably. It will reduce the initial home demand for machinery, which, at a time when engineering works have their order books full and have to quote distant delivery dates, must mean an increase in exports. At the same time, the volume of automatic equipment that has to be imported can be reduced.

Automation is also likely to affect the balance of payments through its influence on the terms of trade. Its possibilities in the sphere of raw-material production are, generally speaking, more limited than in the sphere of manufacturing. For this reason alone, manufacture prices are more likely to be reduced or kept down amidst a general rising trend. The relation between these and raw-material prices is, therefore, liable to change to the detriment of the former as a result of automation. This means that it will become necessary to export more manufactures to pay for the same amount of raw material imports. Moreover, the expansion of production resulting from automation means more demand for raw materials, causing an increase in raw-material prices, and changing the terms of trade even more against industrial countries. Since, however, automation means an increase in the output of manufactures, this effect on the terms of trade should not be viewed with undue concern even from the point of view of manufacturing countries. They will be able to export more in return for their material imports, provided that they can keep domestic consumption under control.

To some extent the effect of automation on the terms of trade and on the import of raw materials tends to offset its effect on the volume of the export and import of manufactures. A country whose rate of automation is high is likely to earn more through its exports of manufactures, and the amount spent on its imports of manufactures is likely to be reduced. On the other hand, it is likely to spend more on its imports of raw materials, not only because its industries will use more, but also because raw-material prices are likely to increase.

The operation of the international price mechanism tends to readjust unduly wide wage differentials between industrial and agricultural countries. The rising trend of raw-material prices resulting from automation enables agricultural and mining undertakings to raise their wages. This is necessary in order to attract more labor to meet the increased demand for raw materials. The demand for labor thus created should create opportunities for the emigration of workers who have become redundant through automation and who are unable to find suitable employment at home.

Automation may create a new set of foreign-exchange problems. Its effect on the terms of trade and on the balance of payments is incalculable, and it adds to the uncertainties of the foreign-exchange outlook. Owing to the creation of wider margins of profits on manufactures, the development of an adverse pressure on the exchanges as a result of price cutting by a progressive rival becomes an ever-present possibility.

Differences in the degree of automation in various countries may upset the fundamental equilibrium upon which the stability of exchanges rests. It may affect purchasing-power parities to such an extent that an adjustment of the exchange parities may appear expedient and even inevitable. But a devaluation need not necessarily be the right answer to the problem created. It is the correct answer when the change in purchasing-power parities is due to a change in the relative degrees of domestic inflation. Discrepancies between the rates of automation in various countries are capable of creating, however, basic structural changes which cannot be dealt with satisfactorily through tampering with parities. If other countries are able to produce the same goods in a good deal fewer man-hours, devaluation does not help the less efficient country, except temporarily.

Devaluation may enable non-automated firms to regain their markets from their automated foreign rivals. But the rise in domestic prices that is bound to follow the devaluation will soon offset this advantage. In order to avoid the loss of foreign markets it would be necessary to repeat the devaluation at relatively frequent intervals. This would undermine confidence in the currency of the country concerned, and an anticipation of the next devaluation would tend to accelerate the rise in prices. As a result the periods of respite purchased at the cost of repeated devaluations would tend to grow shorter and shorter.

In such a situation, acceleration of the progress in automation in the less advanced country is the only lasting remedy. It may become a necessity, an alternative to permanent impoverishment. Under the pressure of foreign competition it may have to be carried out at the wrong moment, when it is bound to affect the national economy in a deflationary sense. For this reason alone, it is important to proceed with automation with the utmost speed while the going is good—that is, amidst the inflationary conditions in an expanding economy, when it can be done largely through an increase of the output instead of having to be done through ruthless reductions in employment.

CHAPTER FIFTEEN

THE THREAT OF
RAW-MATERIAL SHORTAGES

An accelerated production drive to raise the standard of living will defeat its object if it leads to bottlenecks through shortages of raw materials. There is a possibility of the development of such shortages within a country, as a result of an unduly rapid expansion of its production unaccompanied by a corresponding expansion of its exports to pay for its increased imports. There is also a possibility of raw-material shortages on a worldwide scale. Rapid progress of automation, in so far as it is accompanied by considerable expansion of output, may conceivably result in temporary worldwide shortages in essential materials. What is much worse, it might even lead to a complete exhaustion of some irreplaceable materials.

Normally the working of the price mechanism regulates the demand for raw materials and sets automatic forces in motion to discourage their excessive consumption. If, as a result of technological developments, there is a greatly increased demand for a certain material, and the supply is not sufficiently elastic to keep pace with it, a rise in its price tends to discourage the demand. At the same time the rise in its price encourages both exploration for additional sources and research aiming at the invention of substitutes. After an interval supply is likely to catch up with demand and may even cut ahead of it.

The difference that automation makes in this respect is due to the possibility of a sudden substantial increase of demand for certain raw materials. If the increase is gradual, the time lag between it and the adjustment of the supply to the increased demand is relatively short. But if the increase of production through automation results in an unexpectedly steep increase in the demand, shortages may arise before the price mechanism is able to discourage the demand sufficiently, and long before it can effectively stimulate the production of additional supply. It is the suddenness of the increase in the demand which creates the bottlenecks. It gives no time to look round for alternative supplies, nor to carry out research to invent substitutes. Moreover the wide profit margin created by the reduction of the wage bill per unit enables the manufacturers to pay much higher prices for raw materials, so that the rise in prices due to the excess demand does not even begin to discourage their demand until the depletion of the stocks has reached an advanced stage.

Automation may therefore be accompanied by the development of a succession of bottlenecks in various lines of production, leading to pockets of unemployment. What is much worse, it may hasten the complete exhaustion of the world's stock of metals and other materials the supply of which cannot be reproduced. The rate at which such materials are consumed in high-income countries such as the United States is already becoming truly alarming. Although there are still many unexplored areas on the five continents, the possibility of a complete exhaustion of the total resources of the globe of certain minerals must be envisaged in the light of the increase in their consumption during our lifetime. With the increase in the standard of living that is likely to take place within the next quarter of the century, especially in the densely populated backward countries which have been living until now on a bare subsistence level, the day when the last of these resources is used up will be brought considerably nearer. This is all the more likely since the rise in the standard of living of these countries may be accompanied by a rapid increase of their population.

By accelerating the increase of production, automation has contributed, and is expected to contribute much more, towards the exhaustion of irreplaceable materials. The increase in their use is entirely unplanned, so that there is no possibility, at any rate until the process of depletion has reached a much more advanced stage, of establishing some kind of lists of priorities, in order to reserve the scarce supplies for essential requirements. It seems probable that, by the time the need for some co-ordination of requirements is sufficiently realized to make international action practicable, the quantities of the remaining deposits will be very low.

Shortages of supplies that are liable to interrupt the progress of automation and the expansion of production resulting from it may not be confined to the sphere of raw materials. An increase in the supply of electric power is essential for the progress of automation. Power-generating capacity has been increased all over the world since the war, but such is the pace of automation that the growth of demand might easily exceed the rate at which power generation is expanding. The rapidly increasing requirements are liable to outrun the supplies of fuel. It may take twenty years before power generation by means of atomic energy is able to play a sufficiently important part. Meanwhile rapid automation will make increasing demands on the available supply of fuel.

The possibility that expansion of production through automation may be held up even by the limitations of water supplies cannot be ruled out. The volume of water used up by certain industries is very large, and there is no indication that the requirements per unit of output can be reduced by automation. This factor may influence the location of new industries.

The effect of automation on raw-material supplies entails the risk of economic and political friction between the "have" and the "have not" countries. Once the insufficiency of some materials in face of the growing demand comes to be realized, the countries which control the supplies will seek to retain them for their own use. This carries the possibility of conflicts, as the economic prosperity and stability of a country, and even its defenses, may depend on the continuity of the supplies of certain key materials. There is likely to be stockpiling by the countries possessing the sources of such materials long before current requirements have brought them within measurable distance of exhaustion. Embargoes are likely to be placed on the export of scarce materials. This is liable to create much ill feeling between the nations. In this connection it was remarked at a recent conference on automation that the pushbutton factory is liable to lead to pushbutton war.

Already the beginning of a Communist drive to deprive the free countries of some of their raw-material resources has become noticeable. The U.S.S.R. has been employing what are known as "Schachtian devices" to that end. She concludes barter arrangements with raw-material-producing countries. She sells them goods financed by long-term credits, which are repayable in raw-material exports. She even pays the producing countries prices above the world level. Up to the time of writing the total extent to which these devices has been applied has been negligible, but there is a possibility of their much more extensive application.

The maintenance of reasonable relations between supply and demand of essential materials will constitute one of the major tasks of economic statesmanship during coming years. To that end, exploration of new deposits, and exploitation of known but hitherto inaccessible deposits, should be pushed forward long before a dangerous degree of acute shortage arises. Also, the "have not" countries would be wise to stockpile key materials in large quantities. Such materials should be considered as forming part of their gold and foreign exchange reserves. In addition the technically advanced countries with inadequate resources in irreplaceable materials should be pressing forward with their research for substitutes. As and when shortages of supplies, in face of the growing demand, cause the prices of materials to rise, it will in any case become commercially profitable to follow this course.

The world will witness a race between the progress of automation and that of the discovery of new supplies of materials, natural or synthetic. Conceivably the mining of low-grade ores will have to be resorted to, and mineral deposits that are not easily accessible will have to be exploited irrespective of the additional transport cost in money and labor, unless and until suitable substitutes have been invented and are produced in sufficient quantities. Possibly the production of some of the essential substitutes will itself involve considerable capital outlay and current cost. In spite of this, they will have to be produced if there appears to be reason to fear that, as a result of automation, supplies of the natural materials may be exhausted. For this reason alone, it would be bold to make even a tentative forecast about the future requirements of capital and labor. Quite possibly the exploitation of normally uneconomic deposits, the linking up of remote mines by rail and road, and the production of costly substitutes will require so much additional man-hours that it will go a long way towards offsetting any reduction of employment through automation.

CHAPTER SIXTEEN

FISCAL CONSIDERATIONS

OUR task in this chapter is to examine the impact of automation on public finance and fiscal policy. Whether or not automation tends to increase taxation revenue depends on its effect on aggregate cost of production. If automation advances during an inflationary period it usually results in an increase in the aggregate cost of production in spite of a decline in the cost per unit. The resulting increase in the national income means a higher yield of taxation on the basis of unchanged rates of taxation. If, on the other hand, automation is used in such a way as to lead to a reduction of the aggregate cost of production, the accompanying decline in income means a lower yield of taxation, at any rate as far as direct taxation is concerned. An increase in the output of some goods subject to excise tax or some other form of indirect taxation may mean an increase in the yield of such taxes and thus may conceivably offset the decline in the yield of direct taxation. It seems more likely, however, that automation in a contracting economy means a decline in the yield of taxation.

The way in which the benefits of a lower cost of production are allocated between capital and labor is also a factor in influencing the treasury's share in those benefits. To the extent to which the results of the increase in productivity are distributed in higher wages, the treasury's share is likely to be relatively small, because of the low or relatively low rate of direct taxation of lower incomes. In so far as the benefits assume the form of additional profits, the high rate of taxation of corporation earnings and of large personal earnings secures for the treasury the major part of the benefits. In addition, since high profits and high dividends tend to raise the stock-exchange values of the shares, this means a higher yield of stamp duties and of death duties. The former is affected also by a larger turnover that accompanies a rise in stock-exchange prices. Indeed, it may be said without exaggeration that under the prevailing high level of taxation the treasury is the principal financial beneficiary of automation, to the extent to which the benefits are not distributed in the form of higher wages.

The question is whether the treasury is in a position to resist the pressure in favor of higher expenditure that nowadays usually accompanies any rise in revenue. To some extent automation itself entails additional expenditure, for the government has to spend more on scientific and technological research and education. Moreover in case of technological unemployment the government may be called upon to pay more than the standard rate of unemployment relief to the victims of progress. Such additional expenditure as is directly or indirectly connected with automation is likely to be, however, considerably less than the additional revenue derived from it. There is therefore a possibility that, under an expanding economy, automation may lead to a sufficient increase in the yield of taxation to make possible a much-needed reduction in the rate of taxation.

The National Association of Manufacturers put forward, in fact, a plan for a gradual reduction in corporate and individual progressive tax rates over a period of five years, to be financed out of the increased yield of taxation resulting from growing productivity through automation. It expects it to be possible to reduce the maximum rate to 35 per cent by the end of that period. It seems doubtful, however, whether such a degree of reversal of the equalitarian trend would be politically and socially practicable even in the United States, no matter how strong the economic argument may be in favor of increasing the propensity to save by such means.

There is a great deal to be said for the encouragement of automation by fiscal concessions. This is particularly important in Britain, since the level of taxation of profits and dividends is much higher than in the United States and in other industrial countries. High taxation is a strong disincentive, and the lower level of taxation abroad secures a considerable advantage to the competitors of British industries. Moreover, since equalitarianism is less advanced in most industrial countries than in Britain, a larger share of the profits is left with companies for re-investment or for distribution among the higher-income groups which usually provide the risk capital. A less equalitarian distribution of incomes also means that the propensity to save is apt to be higher. This again means that less equalitarian countries are able to proceed with automation at a more rapid rate, because the inflationary effect of the additional investment is not likely to be so strong.

The question whether fiscal differentiation in favor of undistributed profits and against distributed profits serves the interests of automation is a highly controversial one. It aims at inducing companies to retain a larger share of their profit for the purpose of ploughing it back into the industry. More is available for financing the expansion of the existing firms, and they can afford to spend more on research and development. On the other hand, unduly heavy taxation of distributed profits must mean that more will be ploughed back by the well-established firms but less will be available for the establishment of new firms or for the expansion of less well-established firms. This does not necessarily lead to the best use of financial resources from the point of view of automation. A situation may arise in which firms which have already reached the limit of their expansion or the optimum degree of their automation will continue to plough back capital into their business, while firms with ample scope for proceeding further with automation and expansion are prevented from doing so by lack of funds. Their chances of raising funds for that purpose would greatly improve if holders of equities, who are the potential subscribers to issues of new shares, were to receive higher dividends on their existing investments and if their chances of being paid high dividends on new and risky ventures were to increase.

It is essential that industrial firms should be given increased depreciation allowances, in view of the fact that automation means a higher degree of wear and tear and an increased rate of obsolescence. Automatic equipment, because it is highly complicated and because it is to be used more intensively, is likely to wear out in a relatively short time. Owing to the importance of avoiding breakdowns, which would hold up the entire process of production, it is advisable to replace such equipment even before it has actually come to an end of its useful life. Because of the accelerated pace of technological progress, automatic equipment which represents today the last word may become obsolete tomorrow and it may have to be replaced in spite of the high capital loss involved. In the circumstances existing depreciation allowances are far from adequate. Their increase, or the granting of an investment allowance, would be fully justified from a fiscal point of view, for an accelerated application of automation would increase taxation revenue.

Moreover, it would be to the interests of automation to reverse to some degree the equalitarian trend in respect of the taxation of medium-sized personal incomes. Automation means a decline in the use of unskilled labor and an increase in the need for skilled labor. It also means a considerable increase in the need for engineers and research workers. In the absence of undue rigidity in the wage structure, the levels of respective wages and salaries, and the differentials between them, would naturally adapt themselves to the changed requirements. Under the existing system of taxation, however, much of the attraction of a wider differential for the benefit of skilled labor, engineers and research workers is offset by the steeply progressive rate of direct taxation. It is essential that those who have spent years on studying or being trained, in order to be able to fill more difficult jobs calling for specialized knowledge and higher responsibility, should be allowed to retain the additional benefit to which they are entitled. It would be the height of absurdity to continue the present system under which the greater part of what is given to them in the way of higher pay is taken away in taxation. Now that their social and commercial utility has increased, and is likely to continue to increase, it is only reasonable that they should be allowed to enjoy the benefits of automation to which they can contribute so much.

Inventors in particular deserve better treatment. Under the existing system they derive very little encouragement from any bonuses paid to them by their employers, because most of it is taken away in taxation. The *ex gratia* payments made by the British Government for wartime inventions were exempted from income tax and surtax. There is no reason why this principle should not apply to bonuses paid by the government or by private firms for peacetime inventions. Such suggestions are opposed by equalitarians on the ground that it would be contrary to the principles of social justice and equity. If an inventor earned $200,000 by producing a cure for cancer, he would be denounced as a profiteer, and the equalitarians would insist that most of his earnings should be confiscated by taxation. Yet even in the Soviet Union encouragement is provided to inventors and skilled labor in general in the form of higher pay, much of which is not taken back in taxation. From the point of view of the progress of automation, it is essential to treat inventors more generously.

Some measures of reversal of the equalitarian trend would be necessary, not only in order to provide an incentive where incentive is likely to yield the largest benefit to the community, but also in order to raise the propensity to save. Throughout the nineteenth century and until World War II it was thanks to the savings of wealthy classes and middle classes that the expansion of production did not produce an unduly heavy inflationary effect. Such inflation as occurred before 1945 was due for the most part to wars. The inherently inflationary effect of expanding production was more or less offset by the saving of a large proportion of the middle and large incomes. Indeed supporters of underconsumption theories of business cycles were probably right in claiming that there was a tendency for the propensity to save to be excessive, and that this was largely responsible for the relatively slow rate of economic progress and for the economic difficulties of the thirties. Oversaving was probably partly due to the excessive degree of inequality between incomes.

In the meantime, however, the pendulum has swung very much in the opposite direction. Needless to say, this does not mean to suggest that a return to the pre-war state of affairs would be expedient even if it were politically and socially possible. The clock cannot be put back to 1939. From a purely economic point of view we could not return to a system of distribution of income which might involve over-saving, because in doing so we would run the risk of slumps on the pre-war pattern. It is essential to maintain the purchasing power of the masses at a high level so as to enable them to buy the increased output resulting from automation. Otherwise automation would be doomed to lead to over-production. Judging by the degree of nonstop inflation since the war, there must, however, be a fair scope for an increase in income differentials, without running the risk of creating a deflationary situation. Direct taxation should be reduced, and the maximum limit should be fixed well below its present figure. In order to make such a concession acceptable to the workers, it might be expedient in Britain to tax capital gains as well as current earnings, as and when the capital gains are actually realized.

The subject of assisting automation by reducing the inflationary trend was dealt with in Chapter 13 on monetary policy, where it was suggested that to encourage saving the government should initiate the issue of loans with guaranteed purchasing power based on the index of the cost of living, and also lottery loans. Such loans are likely to appeal to the wage-earner, and it is of the utmost importance that a reasonable proportion of their increased earnings should be mopped up by increased saving.

Possibly the low propensity to save is due to the fact that

industrial workers are not used to earning much beyond what is needed to maintain themselves around a bare subsistence level. In a generation or two they may conceivably acquire the saving habits of the middle classes. At that stage the problem of economists and of the authorities will be to devise means by which to increase their propensity to consume and reduce their excessive propensity to save. For the present, however, we have to pursue the opposite aim of encouraging small saving. To that end, it might be advisable to exempt from taxation not only the interest earned on small savings but to some extent even the capital amount that is set aside instead of being spent.

A formula that may deserve consideration in this connection is that if the recipients of the higher wages agree to the investment of the surplus in "post-boom credits" the amounts thus invested should be exempted from taxation altogether. Such credits should bear interest but the principal should remain blocked for an indefinite period, unless the owners of such credits become unemployed. Apart from that, the government would only release them as and when a slackening of consumer demand makes it appear expedient to increase consumer purchasing power. The same principle could be applied also to both undistributed and distributed profits, the blocking of which during periods of boom should be encouraged by fiscal devices.

Most of the above recommendations are likely to be unpopular with the industrial workers. Yet it is evidently to their interests that automation should proceed unhampered by fiscal disincentive or by inflation. Even in more favorably placed countries, such as the United States, the existing system of taxation does not provide the maximum of encouragement to automation. Since the outcome of the "cold war" depends largely on the relative progress made by automation in the United States and in the Soviet Union, it is to the interests of the American people and of the entire free world that the fiscal handicaps to the progress of automation should be removed. Income differentials in the United States are wider than in Britain, but it would serve the interests of economic progress if they could be widened further.

Professor W. Arthur Lewis, a Socialist economist, in his *Theory of Economic Growth,* states: "The climate of our day is hostile to income differentials . . . and to handsome profits in the extreme. These, however, are part of the cost of development." He advocates the acceptance of these differentials as a temporary cost of more rapid growth. These remarks are well worth bearing in mind when considering the fiscal policy that would provide the maximum of encouragement to growth through automation.

CHAPTER SEVENTEEN

WAGE POLICY

THE tendency of wages in a free economy is supposed to be determined by supply and demand in the labor market, tempered by rigidities resulting from collective bargaining. In reality the unions are in a position to keep the supply of labor artificially low, with the aid of restrictive practices. They are also in a position to increase the demand for labor, because by enforcing wage increases they cause an expansion of consumer demand, leading to an expansion of the labor requirement through the resulting increase in the production of consumer goods and of capital goods. So to suggest that wages are determined by the demand for labor amounts to arguing in a vicious circle, that wages are determined by wages. While an increase in the relative prices of any particular category of goods may discourage demand for them, an increase in the price of labor tends to expand demand for it.

During the last century, when the bargaining power of workers was weak, there was a tendency for wages to remain in the vicinity of subsistence level. Fortunately this is no longer so. Now that the bargaining power of workers has become very strong, the level of wages is largely influenced by the extent of profit margins. Evidence of expanding profits usually gives rise to wage demands by employees of the firms or industries which earn higher profits. In a more general way, increasing productivity and a rising cost of living constitute the basis of widespread wage demands.

Automation tends to stimulate wage demands because it increases productivity and also the profit margins of firms directly concerned. It is true that it tends to lower the demand for unskilled labor. Up to the time of writing, this effect has not been sufficiently pronounced in any country to cause a decline in the level of wages, or even to arrest their increase, though it is permissible to suppose that in the absence of automation the scarcity of labor might have been even more acute and the rise in wages even steeper.

Two sets of problems of wage policy arise from automation. They relate to the general level of wages and to differentials between various categories of wages. As wages constitute by far the largest contribution to consumers' purchasing power, it is of the utmost importance that their level should strike the right balance between the need to avoid both inflation and deflation. If wages are not high enough, consumer demand is liable to be deficient; the increased output can only be sold at a lower price; and a deflationary spiral is liable to set in. If the level of wages is too high, the surplus purchasing power will press on the volume of goods, especially as, during a period of rising production, the increase in output is always lagging behind the increase in purchasing power. The result is inflation. The rise in production, by increasing the demand for labor, stimulates new wage demands, justified to some extent by the inflationary effect of the pipeline lag. A wage spiral sets in. It is indeed difficult to avoid an unduly high and constantly rising wage level under conditions of overfull employment.

Automation, by moderating the extent of overfull employment, tends to establish a more normal balance of power between employers and employees. To the extent to which the general trend of wages depends on argument and not on the relative bargaining position of the parties, there seems to be no reason why, in the conditions prevailing since the war, automation should strengthen the case for a general increase in the level of wages, as distinct from increases granted to those employed in automated industries. The argument that higher wages are necessary to correct a deficiency of purchasing power has been clearly inapplicable in postwar conditions. Moreover a rise in the general level of wages granted on the strength of the progress of automation necessarily means the payment of higher wages by industries which have not benefited by automation and have not increased their productivity or profit margin.

There is every economic justification for a general increase of wages to accompany or follow automation, if and when there is evidence of deficiency of consumer purchasing power. Then, and only then, the economic argument calling for additional purchasing power in order that the increased output should be marketable, is valid. Otherwise general wage demands on the ground of higher productivity rest exclusively on social arguments. The argument that higher wages are necessary in order to encourage further automation cannot be used in support of excessive wage claims. After all, had it not been for a previous rise in wages it would not have been worth while for managements to adopt automatic equipment. So it is arguable that labor received its share of the proceeds in anticipation of automation. The weight of economic argument is against a general increase of wages on the ground of higher productivity, so long as the upward trend of prices indicates that consumer purchasing power, so far from being deficient, is actually excessive. Unfortunately the idea of adjusting the level of wages in a counter-cyclical sense, by granting wage increases where there is a slackening trend of business and refusing wage increases when business conditions are booming, is not practicable. This fact strengthens the case for "post-boom credits," advocated in the last chapter, as a means of equalizing the purchasing power of wage-earners in periods of booms and depressions.

In the absence of some such device, and given the low propensity to save, responsibility for exercising self-restraint in wage demands, for the sake of avoiding advanced inflation that might lead to drastic measures causing unemployment, must be placed fairly and squarely on the shoulders of the unions. As Professor Hicks pointed out in his Presidential Address delivered to Section F of the British Association at Bristol in 1955, instead of being on a gold standard, we are on a labor standard. The value of money is determined by the level of wages; the quantity of money and the level of prices have to adjust themselves to the level of wages, in the same way as they had to adjust themselves to the amount of the gold reserve under the gold standard. It means that union leaders are fully as responsible for the economic stability and prosperity of the entire community as Central Bankers were in the old days. The power is less concentrated but none the less real.

In addition to problems relating to the general wage level, automation may also give rise to problems of wage differentials, (a) between skilled and unskilled labor, (b) between labor employed in automated and non-automated sectors of the same firm, (c) between automated and non-automated firms within the same industry, and (d) between automated and non-automated industries.

As and when industries become automated, their need for unskilled labor falls and their need for skilled labor rises. Automation also means a strong increase in the demand for engineers and scientific workers. It should be the object of a wage policy to allow the development of sufficiently wide differentials between the various categories of wages and salaries to induce a sufficient number of people to acquire the necessary training for jobs requiring skilled labor and for engineering and scientific work. During the postwar period there has been a distinct trend towards equalitarianism not only between employees and capitalists, or between working classes on the one hand and middle and upper classes on the other, but also between the various grades within the same groups of classes of employees. Partly on the basis of reasonable social arguments in favor of improving the lot of the lowest-paid workers, but largely by the weight of their numbers, the unskilled laborers have succeeded in reducing the pre-war differential between the level of wages for skilled and unskilled labor. In more recent years skilled labor has made an effort to obtain the restoration of the pre-war differentials, by securing wage increases of an extent that employers could not afford to grant to the large number of unskilled or semi-skilled labor. Although employers were usually in sympathy with such claims, they encountered difficulties on account of the efforts of unskilled labor to maintain the postwar differential unchanged.

This conflict of interests is likely to be accentuated as a result of automation. In the industries directly affected there will be an increase in the number of jobs requiring advanced training and intelligence. The scarcity value of such employees is bound to rise unless technical education and training schemes succeed in producing a larger number of them. If the wage differentials are not sufficiently wide, there is not adequate inducement for young people to take up skilled work involving years of preliminary training. It is too tempting for them to earn a living wage from the day when they leave school, or when they have completed their military service. They can get married in their early twenties on present-day wages for unskilled labor, and settled down to tolerable existence, even if their prospects of advancement are limited. The additional remuneration earned after years of training is in many instances not sufficient inducement, except to those who happen to be keen on doing skilled work in preference to routine work. Unless the resistance of the unions of unskilled workers to a widening of differentials can be overcome, their maintenance at the present level would effectively hinder automation by keeping skilled labor permanently in short supply.

The relative strength of the small unions representing skilled labor will be likely to increase in the industries affected by automation. Even so, strikes by unskilled labor are liable to bring production to a standstill, owing to the all-but-universal adoption of the attitude that to do the work of strikers in any conceivable circumstances is one of the deadly sins. Even if the strike over differentials is directed primarily against the skilled laborers and not against employers, the skilled laborers themselves usually refuse to step into the breach by undertaking the work of unskilled laborers. The result is a deadlock which is often very difficult to break.

Increased automation will probably be accompanied by a number of such awkward strikes over differentials. The only hope for avoiding the resulting losses would be the adoption of a wage policy approved by the workers themselves through their industrial and political organizations. From a political point of view this is in the interests of the British Labour movement, because if Socialist Parties identify themselves with the interests of the lower-paid workers they will drive the skilled laborers into the arms of their political opponents. There is indeed a tendency for higher-paid skilled labor in Britain to regard themselves as belonging to the middle classes and to vote Conservative, partly because they feel that the Labour Party's excessive equalitarianism is against their interests. This tendency, which must have been largely responsible for the Conservative victory at two consecutive General Elections, is likely to gather strength, unless the Socialists succeed in persuading the unions representing unskilled labor to consent to a widening of differentials.

Notwithstanding political considerations, such unions are likely to resist a widening of differentials. In effect, if not in intention, the result of this attitude is to delay automation, because the additional pay to skilled labor is not sufficient to attract a sufficient number of people. A strike against a widening of differentials is, therefore, almost as effective a weapon to resist automation as a strike directed against the installation of automatic equipment.

The only way in which difficulties arising from resistance to a widening of differentials can be overcome is for the Government and employers to finance extensively the training of skilled labor. It might become necessary and expedient to give the trainees full pay either at public expense or at the expense of the firms directly concerned. This is already being done by many firms, and a general adoption of the scheme would go a long way towards securing the required numbers in spite of the inadequacy of wage differentials. Even so, a widening of differentials would be necessary as an incentive. Automated firms should be placed in a position to hold out prospects of higher pay to skilled workers.

At the Conference of the Institute of Production Engineers in 1955 Mr. F. Garner drew attention to the anomalies that arise when a factory is partly automated, so that some workers have to continue to work in the old section while others are employed in much more satisfactory working conditions in the automated section. In view of the labor saved in the automated section, its workers feel they have a strong claim for wage increases. To differentiate for their benefit is bound to cause ill feeling, however, in view of the fact that, in addition to getting higher pay, they work in much more favorable conditions. There is justification for a differential in their favor in so far as their work calls for superior skill. As Mr. Garner points out, the only satisfactory solution for the friction that frequently arises in such a situation is a complete automation of the entire factory. Meanwhile the workers in the non-automated section should also be given a fair share in the increased proceeds of production, so as to allay their discontent.

Problems of differentials arise also from the different degree of automation by various firms within the same industry. In so far as wage agreements are negotiated on a national or regional basis, increases granted under pressure by workers of automated factories are liable to place the less progressive firms at a considerable disadvantage. The most acceptable solution in such circumstances would be to reckon basic wage rates in such a way as to enable even non-automated firms to work profitably; any participation of workers of the automated firms in the increased profits should assume the form of bonuses, subsidized charges in canteens, and other amenities.

Automation is bound to result in wider wage differentials between various industries. In conditions of labor scarcity this necessarily means a transfer of manpower from non-automated to automated industries in so far as the latter need additional workers. An increase of pay in the progressive industries necessarily leads to wage demands also in the static industries and even in the declining industries, especially if their manpower is drained away by the attraction of higher pay in automated industries. To retain sufficient labor to be able to carry on, managements have to concede wage demands which are entirely unjustified on grounds of productivity or profit margins. For instance, although the British Railways are a declining industry which is losing ground all the time to road traffic, their services are indispensable to the national economy, and for this reason they have to concede wage demands, partly in order to avoid strikes which would paralyze the nation, and partly because they have to retain an adequate staff in face of the drain caused by the higher pay received in dynamic industries.

There is also the problem of the increasing need for engineers of various kinds. Their number too will have to be increased materially, in order to ensure the progress and smooth working of automation. Their real earnings, as those of the rest of the middle classes, have declined considerably below pre-war level, largely as a result of taxation, but also because their salaries have not kept pace with the rise in the cost of living. In view of the increasing importance of engineers in the automatic age, it is essential that they should be treated generously both by industry and by the taxation authorities.

Scientific workers in laboratories, research stations, and universities are, generally speaking, very inadequately remunerated. The universities in particular are gravely handicapped by inadequate funds. Moreover, in their case, as in the case of educational establishments in general, the salaries of science teachers has to bear some relation to the general level of salaries of the rest of the teaching staff. Many science teachers have felt impelled, as a result of their financial difficulties, to give up their profession and join research departments of industrial firms. Even many of the latter do not pay sufficiently high salaries to their research staffs. Generally speaking, the salaries of senior research workers and engineers compare very unfavorably with those of senior members of commercial and advertising staffs. There can be no justification for this and the technologists have a genuine grievance. Scientific workers employed by the government on atomic research and other vital research are also very badly paid. The inadequate number of competent teachers of science and technology hinders the training of the required number of engineers.

CHAPTER EIGHTEEN

CONTROL OR FREEDOM?

THE attitude governments should adopt towards automation is probably the most controversial aspect of a subject bristling with controversy. At the one extreme there is the left-wing view—not confined to Communists—that, having regard to the unsettling effect of automation and the possible dangers it entails, its progress greatly strengthens the case for the public ownership of industry. At the other extreme there is the view expressed in the Report of the Congressional Sub-committee on Economic Stabilization that the situation and prospects arising from automation call for no fresh government action in the form of legislation, and that the government's task is confined to standing aside to allow automation to develop unhampered by any restraint.

In his evidence before the Congressional Subcommittee, Reuther said that, although the labor-union movement welcomes automation, "if we subscribe to the *laissez-faire* belief that these things work themselves out, untold harm can be done to millions of innocent people, and to the whole structure of our economy and our free society." On the other hand, Munce, giving evidence on behalf of the National Association of Manufacturers, declared, "Automation clearly will be a blessing to the nation if it is allowed to grow by natural economic selection, and if it is not distorted by unwise and unnecessary effort to thwart its effect. . . . Concern

for the long-range over-all good of the nation and of its people should take precedence over selfish jockeying for special
advantage, or throwing road blocks in the path of automation by demanding advanced commitments to labor." There
are of course intermediate suggestions of various shades
between these two extremes.

In order to make out as strong a case as possible for public
ownership, left-wing writers greatly exaggerate the dangers
to the welfare of workers which they consider to be inherent
in automation. According to them, it is perfectly safe to
proceed with automation in a socialist community where the
workers' interests are duly safeguarded, but automation constitutes a menace to the workers in a capitalist community.

Yet, what are the facts? In the United States and in Britain,
automation is carried out in circumstances in which unemployment through redundancy is reduced to a minimum.
Indeed, in many instances the progress of automation has
been slowed down considerably because of the endeavor to
avoid dismissals. Those who have to be dismissed as a result
of the adoption of labor-saving equipment are usually treated
with much consideration and generosity, and are given an
opportunity to obtain training for other jobs. Rather than
dismiss redundant workers, many firms in capitalist countries
—acting admittedly, under union pressure—agree to "feather-
bedding" practices under which the workers remain on the
payroll even if their continued employment ceases to be
justified.

Admittedly, public ownership of the entire industry would
greatly simplify the solution of many problems arising from
automation. On the other hand it would create many other
problems, whether in connection with automation or in a
general way. It seems to be most unlikely that the electorate

in the United States or in other democratic countries would ever allow itself to be influenced in favor of Communism, even if pro-Communist propaganda succeeded in making the majority believe that in a Communist country it is possible to have it both ways—that automation could make better progress under a totalitarian regime, and that, notwithstanding this, its consequences would be less detrimental to the interests of the working classes. Few workers in democratic countries would be prepared to barter away their human rights—free speech, free vote, free choice of work and, above all, freedom from constant supervision by police spies—in return for such advantages.

At the other extreme, the American attitude favors a policy of unmitigated *laissez faire*. According to this view, automation is able to make the best progress with the least friction if it is allowed to proceed unhampered by any form of government interference. Even social measures in mitigation of individual hardship to those rendered superfluous by the new equipment are opposed in many quarters, where it is felt that the victims must fend for themselves and that they could and should find other employment in the ordinary way. According to this school, any exceptional social assistance would only delay the process of re-allocation of labor.

Even the advocates of the free play of economic forces are in favor of fiscal measures and government expenditure to encourage automation. They urge a reduction of corporation taxation, and also government support for technological education, research, and retraining schemes to upgrade unskilled labor. They are also in favor of a monetary policy that provides adequate funds for financing the capital expenditure involved in automation. There is, therefore, no question of advocating a complete "neutralism" of the government.

Those favoring some intermediate solution would like to go further away from absolute nonintervention. They would like to maintain or restore a measure of control over capital expenditure in order that the government should be able to regulate the pace of automation. Their argument is that, in doing so, the authorities would be able to mitigate the unwanted effects that automation is liable to produce, whether in the form of unemployment or of inflation through excessive investment. Some of them are in favor of co-ordination, in some form, under government auspices, in order that automation should proceed according to some preconceived plan rather than in a haphazard way. This is considered necessary in order to avoid bottlenecks through shortages in raw materials or electric power, also in order to safeguard the less progressive firms from being bankrupted by the more dynamic firms. The latter end could be approached by some method of synchronizing the progress of automation within the same industry. This should be done, according to some, not only on a national scale but also on an international scale, to avoid an automation race with all its disturbing effects on the balance of payments.

Others who would not be prepared to go so far are in favor of regulating the progress of automation by means of selective credit control, in addition to the more conventional monetary devices. By such means it would be possible to prevent a too-rapid progress and to establish a list of priorities on the basis of which industries ripe for automation would take their turn, instead of all industries trying to proceed at the same time. The same device of selective credit control is favored by others as a means to the opposite end—the acceleration of automation by earmarking the limited financial labor or material resources for its requirements, to the detriment of the static industries.

Another form of government intervention which is advocated in some quarters is statutory dividend restraint to ensure the ploughing-back of profits for the requirements of automation. Yet another suggestion favors official pressure to induce industrial firms to pass on to the consumer a large proportion of the benefits of automation in the form of price cuts. Under such a policy, appeals for voluntary action would be reinforced by various fiscal measures suggested in the last chapter.

Government intervention to check inflation by means of credit restrictions is inevitably detrimental to the progress of automation. This consideration appears to strengthen the case for nonmonetary measures, such as physical controls, in preference to monetary disinflationary measures. Physical controls, unless accompanied by monetary disinflation, may enable a country to inflate with impunity for some time, but sooner or later monetary measures will become inevitable. While physical controls as a substitute for monetary control would not serve the interests of automation, in given circumstances there is a strong case for supplementary control in order to reduce the adverse effects of the disinflationary drive on automation.

The government could safeguard the interests of those firms which are willing to automate but are unable to raise the necessary funds, by providing financial facilities for them. The case for such intervention would be particularly strong if official pressure caused the more progressive firms to make drastic price reductions. The government could not disclaim responsibility in such circumstances. Unless the less progressive firms were enabled to modernize their equipment, they would be driven out of business as a direct consequence of government action without which the more progressive firms might have maintained a sufficiently wide profit margin to enable the less progressive firms to continue. It would be, therefore, the government's moral duty to safeguard these firms from the effects of its policy.

Speedy and smooth progress of automation largely depends on the ability of striking a happy medium between excessive control and complete absence of control. Ideological dogmatism in either sense is out of place when so much is at stake.

CHAPTER NINETEEN

SOCIAL CONSIDERATIONS

THE relative influence of social considerations on the determination of economic policies has increased considerably
since the war. For this reason, among others, the social aspects
of automation are of great importance. If it appeared probable that automation would result in large-scale technological unemployment, its progress would encounter resistance
on economic as well as social grounds. The social and economic points of view are liable to clash, however, if automation is expected to entail a degree of unemployment and
other human hardship which, while presenting a major social
problem, is not sufficiently widespread or sufficiently lasting
to present also a major economic problem. Accordingly, in
such a situation, our attitude towards automation would be
influenced by the relative importance we attach to economic
and social considerations. At the one extreme there are those
who would prefer to forgo the immense economic advantages of automation for fear that it might mean temporary
inconvenience for a relatively large number of workers and
lasting hardship for a small number of them. At the other
extreme there are those who shrug indifferent shoulders at
the thought of hardships to a small fraction of the community,
and believe in the cynical slogan that "one cannot make an
omelette without breaking eggs."

The widespread fears of the hardships that automation

may cause to individual victims are understandable on the basis of the experience of the Industrial Revolution. It is true that the deplorable human suffering it entailed is now a matter of the past, while the lasting economic benefits it brought are enjoyed today by every man, woman and child. Even so, potential victims of the "Second Industrial Revolution" must be forgiven if they do not derive much comfort from the thought that future generations will consider their sufferings as the necessary price that had to be paid for the sake of the high standard of living which those generations will enjoy. What is, or should be, much more comforting to them than the gratitude of posterity is the fact that fundamental changes have taken place since the period of the Industrial Revolution. Thanks to those changes, victims of a "Second Industrial Revolution" are not exposed to hardships comparable with those suffered by the victims of progress of a century ago.

Today democratic countries have systems of social security undreamed of in the nineteenth century. Even if unemployment benefits do no more than maintain the victims of progress on a bare subsistence level, they save them from the worst hardships to which their forerunners were exposed.

Today we have universal suffrage. Any government that would tolerate a substantial and lasting increase of unemployment would lose votes—not only those of the unemployed themselves but also those of the many times larger numbers who envisage the possibility that their turn might come. The adverse political effects of a large-scale technological unemployment would cut across classes, and the government responsible for it would lose the support of vital floating votes.

Today the industrial balance of power is quite different from what it was in the nineteenth century. The unions now possess immense power. They are in a position to prevent automation taking place in circumstances that would inflict disadvantages on a large number of their members. They can, and often do, slow down the rate of automation and only give way in return for various safeguards.

Today the employers themselves are more conscious of their social responsibilities than were the "hard-faced businessmen" of the Industrial Revolution. Nor can they ignore altogether the more humane conception that has developed in public opinion.

Above all, today, owing to the existence of a high degree of employment, there are incomparably better opportunities for the re-employment of victims of automation. Indeed, in the conditions prevailing since the end of the war, given adequate mobility of unemployed labor, any unemployment is likely to be purely local and temporary. Pockets of unemployment may exist concurrently with a continued shortage of labor in other industries or in other districts. But, provided that unemployed workers are willing to change their occupation or their location, they can easily step from one job straight into another.

This last consideration is of particular importance. While the possibility of large-scale unemployment arising from non-technological causes cannot be excluded altogether, the extent of technological unemployment through automation at a predictable rate will probably not even be sufficient in Britain to liquidate overfull employment altogether. All it is likely to do is to mitigate the scarcity of labor to some extent. The unemployed, instead of having the choice between three or four vacancies, may only be able to choose between two. Or, if the worst comes to the worst, the number of vacancies may decline to the figure of unemployed. Even such a degree of reduction of employment is likely to be resisted by those who are, naturally enough, reluctant to lose the advantages of their scarcity value.

The state of affairs is somewhat different in the United States where the unemployed were still numbered in millions during the prosperous fifties. They are confined, however, mostly to certain depressed areas, while elsewhere conditions similar to those in Britain appear to have developed. It is safe to assume that, with the memories of the mass-unemployment of the thirties still very much alive, the United States Government would not hesitate to intervene to check any substantial increase of unemployment.

The aims that social policy can pursue in face of the possibility of a moderate degree of technological unemployment arising from automation may be summarized as follows:

(1) Prevention or mitigation of unemployment: (a) by slowing down the progress of automation, (b) by guaranteed annual employment agreements, (c) by "feather-bedding" practices, (d) by reducing working hours.

(2) Absorption of the unemployed: (a) by employment-creating government measures, (b) by inflationary policies accentuating the general demand for labor, (c) by increasing the flexibility of labor.

(3) Reducing hardships caused by unemployment or change of employment: (a) by longer notices for dismissals, (b) by compensation payments, (c) by supplementary relief, (d) by priorities at labor exchanges, (e) by transference of pension rights, (f) by retraining.

It is the policy of many unions to fight a delaying action against automation to slow down its rate of progress. According to one estimate, so long as technological unemployment created by automation does not exceed about two per cent per annum, the barring of manufacturing industries to new entrants would solve the problem, because the annual rate of normal retirement is about two per cent. So a successful effort to keep down the rate of automation would effectively prevent unemployment. This device would delay progress and would defeat its object. It plays into the hands of more progressive rivals whose rapid advance may create unemployment through obsolescence in the less progressive country.

The adoption of the system of guaranteed annual wages by a number of firms in the United States constitutes one of the effective devices of the American unions in certain industries. If confined to employees with a certain period of service, this system is not without advantages to employers. It tends to discourage the unduly high rate of labor turnover caused by frequent changes of employment for inadequate reasons.

The most frequently attempted device is for workers to insist that, in spite of the adoption of labor-saving equipment, the same number of workers should be retained. Such "feather-bedding" is a very effective obstacle to automation, unless the additional capital outlay is intended for an increase of output rather than a reduction of the aggregate cost of producing the existing output, in which case the total number of employees need not be reduced.

There is a strong case against feather-bedding both from an economic and from a social point of view. It hinders the much-needed re-allocation of labor which would relieve the scarcity of manpower in non-automated industries, and it thus prevents automation from indirectly assisting non-automated industries. Dismissals for redundancy are only deferred as a result of such arrangements. For, the moment there is a business recession, the firms can no longer afford to keep unnecessary workers, and the unions cease to be in a sufficiently strong bargaining position to prevent their dismissal. Feather-bedding may mean that the workers, instead of being dismissed during a boom when they could easily find alternative employment, have to be dismissed during a slump when there is no hope for their early re-employment. Moreover, while during a boom they are likely to be treated generously by their employers, during a slump, when business firms find it difficult to make ends meet, they are not likely to receive anything beyond what they are legally entitled to under their contract.

The long-term safeguard against unemployment through automation is the reduction of working hours. The American unions set the thirty-hour week as their target. The trend is in keeping with the requirements of progress, as a rising standard of living means not only increasing consumption but also more leisure. The danger is that unwarranted anxiety to avoid unemployment may lead to premature or excessive curtailment of working hours, resulting in an accentuation of the scarcity of labor in spite of automation.

The same end can be achieved also by general inflationary devices leading to an all-round increase of demand for goods and therefore to an increase of demand for labor. Encouragement of investment, release of consumer purchasing power by tax concessions, relaxation of credit restrictions, acceleration of government capital projects, are among the inflationary measures by which technological unemployment can be dealt with.

A much more constructive policy is to increase the flexibility of labor. This can be achieved by a variety of devices. Amidst prevailing conditions of housing shortage, a most important device is the provision of alternative housing facilities to workers who, having lost their jobs through automation, would have an opportunity of re-employment in another district. Such workers should be given absolute priority by housing authorities, and housing drives should aim at constructing a certain amount of reserve accommodation for the sake of achieving flexibility of labor.

Another device is the provision of cheap and convenient transport facilities to workers who have to cover longer distances as a result of their re-employment. During World War II tax concessions were made in Britain to that end, but they were confined to those directly concerned with the war effort. The same principle should now be applied to victims of automation. But in itself it would not go far enough to compensate them for any increased transport costs.

To the extent to which some degree of technological unemployment through automation cannot be prevented, and the re-employment of all victims cannot be speedily ensured, the next best thing is to mitigate hardships whenever they occur. This can be done by inducing employers to give longer notice in case of redundancy dismissals so as to give the workers a better chance to look round for alternative employment. In view of the saving in cost effected through automation, most automated firms could afford to do that. Likewise they may be able and willing to agree to severance payments to compensate their employees for the hardships they suffer through no fault of their own. Alternatively, redundant employees could be granted long leave with full pay or part pay for the purpose of enabling them to train themselves for other work. The employers themselves may provide for retraining schemes. Early retirement of the older workers with full pension would be another practicable device.

The extent of the sacrifices that employers are prepared to

make to mitigate hardships must depend on various considerations, such as, for instance, length of the service of the
dismissed employee. It would be unfair to treat a lifelong
employee in the same way as the latest newcomer who
changes his job several times a year. The principle that new-
comers should be the first to go has at times been insisted
upon by the majority of workers, but its too rigid application would be inexpedient, because it would discourage new
entries.

The government, for its part, could contribute by granting
a supplementary unemployment relief to victims of automation. Their case is somewhat different from the unemployed
in general, because it is they who pay the price for progress.

A device that would reduce hardship would be the transference of pension claims. Under existing practice, employees
lose their claims under private pension schemes—apart from
the refunding of their own contributions—if they leave their
firms. There has been much talk about making pension
claims generally transferable from one firm to another. It is
to be feared, however, that any such measure would further
increase the already excessive rate of turnover of workers,
and would be therefore detrimental to efficiency. But the
technologically unemployed are a class apart. They are dismissed, not because they are unsatisfactory, or because trade
is bad, but because they are replaced by machines. In such
circumstances there is everything to be said for safeguarding
their interests as far as practicable. In any case, they stand
to lose the benefit of their acquired skill, their seniority and
status, and the goodwill built up by working with the same
firm for years. So the least they could reasonably expect is
that their full pension claims should be at any rate safeguarded.

Retraining schemes are of the utmost importance. This is largely a matter for the government, but firms anxious to secure labor should be willing to undertake the training of workers dismissed through automation. In many instances such training courses would result in the upgrading of unskilled workers. But in many other instances a change of employment might entail, for semi-skilled or skilled workers, a permanent loss of the use of old skill and earning capacity in spite of their re-training.

The effect of automation on wages and prices has already been discussed. The increased purchasing power of the lower-income groups, whether through higher wages or lower prices, is not the only way, however, in which automation causes social betterment. An equally important way is the increase of leisure. In the long run, increased productivity is bound to lead to a reduction of working hours. But excessive and premature insistence on that solution is liable to reduce materially the benefits of automation in the form of larger output. As we shall see in the next chapter, apart from the unsatisfied needs of lower-income groups in the industrial countries, which should be met to a reasonable degree before any drastic cuts in working hours, there are also almost unlimited requirements in underdeveloped countries which ought to be met. To relax the drive for increased output before the essential needs of hundreds of millions on a starvation level are covered, and before backward countries are provided with capital goods to a reasonable degree, would be a most selfish attitude on the part of the workers of the more advanced countries.

Cuts in working hours may become necessary as a temporary way of spreading a reduced amount of work among all employees. This device would be a preferable alternative to unemployment. But so long as there is scarcity of labor in many industries, there is no economic justification for it as it prevents the much-needed reallocation of labor. Even from a purely social point of view, it might be better in the long run to inflict on a minority the inconvenience and hardship of having to change occupation and location, and of being downgraded, rather than keep down the productive capacity of the community by a premature lowering of working hours. Even in the United States, notwithstanding the high standard of living, much remains to be accomplished before there can be justification for a relaxation of efforts. "We do still have in this country," declared the Report of the Congressional Subcommittee on Economic Stabilization, "substantial groups of comparatively underprivileged and lower-income groups, who should be remembered before those in the more favored industries can conscientiously turn to a shortened work day or longer weekend."

Moreover, shorter hours cannot always be confined to automated firms. They are often applied uniformly for the same industry by nationwide or regional agreements, which means that those who cannot afford to automate might be driven out of business. The result would be unemployment and enforced change of employment on a large scale.

Automation may provide increased leisure in a different way. During recent years the acute scarcity of labor induced many employers to tempt people who were above retiring age to remain at work or to resume work. In view of the increased average expectation of life resulting from improved conditions, it is now widely considered to be a good thing if older people are provided with the option of remaining in harness. In certain occupations they could carry on well beyond the statutory or conventional retiring age. But, when all is said and done, there is much to be said against depriving the older generation of its well-earned leisure. As a result of automation, younger workers may be released from industry and may become available for the lighter tasks for which old people are now being increasingly enlisted. At the same time, thanks to increased productivity, it will become possible to pay higher retirement benefits, so that there should be less inducement for old people to continue to work after reaching retiring age.

The beneficial social effects of automation include the improved conditions of safety and hygiene, the reduction of risk to life and limb, the reduction of drudgery and fatigue. Automation will contribute towards a further extension of the expectation of life.

Automation has in fact considerably reduced the rate of accidents. In his Annual Report for 1954 the Chief Inspector of Factories for Great Britain lays considerable stress on this fact. "We in the Factory Department," the Report states, "are watching the development of automation with considerable interest. We can see that eventually it will influence the cleanliness of the factory and increase its safety because the machine will be remote from its human supervisor. Automatic handling . . . eliminates many accidents due to handling goods or materials." The Chief Inspector quotes the example of a sugar-beet refinery in which a certain plant is now operated by one man on each shift instead of six as previously. "Before, work was heavy and hot, but work at the new plant is done sitting down in front of the automatic electronic control nicknamed 'the piano'." There can be no doubt that automation saves a great deal of fatigue.

In the United States, too, the decline of accident rate is impressive. According to D. S. Harder, Executive Vice-

President of the Ford Motor Company and one of the leading experts on automation, the accident rates declined at the Ford works between 1947 and 1950 from 10.3 disabling injuries per million man-hours to 1.97, a decline of 81 per cent. In 1947, 0.84 days were lost through accidents per thousand days of work. Three years later the loss was reduced to 0.28 days, a decline of 67 per cent.

One way in which automation will tend to reduce the period of active work is through necessitating prolonged training of large numbers of engineers and skilled workers. This may necessitate the raising of the school-leaving age and the provision of facilities for higher technological education for large numbers of people. It is equally important, however, to provide those already in the industry with adequate opportunity to upgrade themselves by means of additional training.

Even after allowing for all these advantages it would be impossible to deny that automation may mean hardship and risk of unemployment or downgrading to a by no means insignificant section of the working classes. Without trying to minimize the disadvantages involved, it is permissible to remind those who are inclined to exaggerate them that the broader interests of the community as a whole occasionally demand sacrifices from the individual. The burden of the war was not equitably spread among the whole populations of the belligerent countries. More often than not the compensation paid to the owners of property acquired by compulsory purchase made in the public interest is not sufficient to enable them to acquire property of equal value at the prevailing market prices, so that they suffer a financial loss, quite apart from the inconvenience caused by being deprived of their homes. The argument used in justification of this unfair practice is the overriding public interest. The same argument is valid when a limited number of individuals are exposed to inconvenience and hardship in the interests of progress through automation.

Any attempt to provide watertight safeguards for all individuals against dismissal through automation would introduce a degree of rigidity in the labor market—comparable with the rigidity of the system of castes in ancient Egypt, or of the medieval guilds—that would greatly reduce the possibility of progress. "Organized labor should continue to recognize," states the Report of the Congressional Subcommittee, "that an improved level of living for all cannot be achieved by a blind defense of the *status quo*." The same Report clearly states, however, the corollary to this proposition in the following terms: "Technological change cannot be regarded as progress at all if it is not able to pay its own way, not merely in the junking of old machinery but by giving due recognition to the human costs of retaining and readjustment."

Admittedly, even though only an insignificant minority of employees may be directly affected, it is impossible to foresee who precisely the victims are likely to be, so that automation tends to create a feeling of uncertainty for a much larger number of workers. This is beyond doubt on the debit side of automation. Moreover the replacement of man by machine is liable to weaken the bargaining power of unions that have been artificially strengthened by the postwar scarcity of labor. This means that organized labor as a whole is called upon to give up some of the advantages it has gained at the expense of the rest of the community in return for future advantages, to be shared with the community. This undoubtedly involves immediate sacrifice in return for future gains. But, in weighing these sacrifices, it is necessary to bear in mind what industrial workers have already received from the community since the war.

A more serious social problem than the effect of automation on the industrial worker is its effect on office workers. In their case the risk of unemployment on a large scale is much more substantial. It is true that, in an expanding economy, there is room even for increased office staffs side by side with the newly installed electronic computers. The evidence before the Congressional Subcommittee quotes some concrete instances—referred to in Chapter 7—in which employers actually added to their office staffs after automation. But it would be unduly optimistic to generalize from such instances. As and when computers become cheaper and more popular, large numbers of clerks will undoubtedly become redundant. And while displaced factory workers stand a good chance of finding alternative employment in other factories, the popularization of the electronic computer may reduce materially the total requirements of office workers. This might mean that clerks would have to take up factory work in large numbers. In view of the higher degree of intelligence required for many factory jobs as a result of automation, they provide an excellent material for being trained for the new type of skilled labor which calls for no physical exertions that would be beyond their capacity. What is perhaps equally important, the elimination of dirty and arduous tasks from factory work will go a long way towards removing the class distinction between office worker and factory worker. The latter too may even be able to wear a white collar, that somewhat overrated symbol of genteel middle-class "respectability."

In any case, the reduction in the number of clerks is a

healthy development. Their proportion to factory workers has increased too much in recent times. It seems that automation is likely to reverse this trend. Deplorable as this may be from the point of view of many clerks, who may have to undergo, very much against their wish, a much more drastic change of occupation than industrial workers rendered redundant by automation, it is to the public interest that this sacrifice should be inflicted on them for the sake of progress.

In order to mitigate the social disadvantages of automation it is necessary for employers, unions and the government to co-operate closely and to show a high degree of understanding of each other's point of view. Much attention must be paid to the human problems involved. It is understandable if the unions are reluctant to consent to a degree of automation which is liable to inflict immediate disadvantages on their members. It is equally understandable if employers, when dealing with unemployment problems arising from automation, are often reluctant to go beyond the letter of their collective agreements with the unions, having regard to the hard bargaining with which they had to contend in recent years, and to the large percentage of their profits appropriated by the government for welfare-state financing. Yet a display of a spirit of understanding on their part should go a long way towards reducing union opposition to automation, even if it cannot be eliminated altogether.

CHAPTER TWENTY

HOW UNDERDEVELOPED
COUNTRIES ARE AFFECTED

THE question of the development of economically backward countries has gained considerable prominence since the end of the Second World War. Until recently the "inevitability of gradualness" of their progress was almost universally taken for granted. Both the peoples themselves and peoples more favorably placed had assumed that underdeveloped areas were to remain poor and backward for a very long time to come. It had been assumed that the inhabitants of underdeveloped countries were doomed to remain at or even slightly under subsistence level, owing to the rate at which their numbers tended to increase in response to any economic improvement.

During the forties and fifties, however, the attitude of world opinion, and also feelings in the countries directly concerned, underwent a drastic change. World conscience has at last been stirred by the growing contrast between the rapidly rising standard of living in advanced countries and the virtually stagnant conditions in backward countries. Increasing productivity in the former induced many people to revise their opinion that nothing whatever could be done to hasten the progress of the many hundreds of millions of backward peoples. Relaxation of the financial limitations to increasing production must have contributed towards this change of opinion. Within the advanced countries it has already greatly mitigated that "poverty amidst plenty," a problem which had been considered to be incapable of practical solution before the war. This change has given rise to hopes that what has proved to be possible in respect of the depressed classes in advanced countries might become practicable also in respect of the many times more numerous and much poorer depressed classes in backward countries.

Accordingly various plans for the economic and technological assistance of the backward countries have been elaborated since the war. American assistance under Truman's Point Four, the Colombo Plan, the British Colonial Development and Welfare scheme, etc., have made a good beginning. Owing to the vast number of the peoples involved, the many millions of dollars and pounds they received were, however, mere drops in the ocean. It is evident that a great deal more would have to be done before economic assistance by the advanced countries could make an appreciable difference to the standard of living of the backward countries. In fact, it has even been stated on high authority that all the efforts at assistance have barely succeeded in maintaining their low standard of living in face of the postwar increase in their populations.

To be able to help underdeveloped countries effectively on the basis of the existing level of productivity would involve very heavy sacrifices on the part of advanced peoples. Indeed the degree of sacrifice that would be required would be entirely impracticable. Before the war it might have been possible to make ignorant people believe that the superfluities of wealthy classes in advanced countries could feed the starving millions in backward countries. Even then a little statistical thinking combined with elementary common sense would have reduced this contention to absurdity. Today, however, the equalitarian trend in respect of incomes in

advanced countries has reached such a stage that the extent
to which the greater half of mankind could be fed just by
"soaking the rich" would be obviously quite negligible. They
could only be helped to any appreciable extent today if the
lower-income groups in advanced countries, which receive
between them by far the larger proportion of the national
income, were to contribute their share in the assistance by
consenting to a really substantial reduction in their standard
of living. That would be the only possible way of releasing
a considerable proportion of goods for the purpose of assisting the masses of less-fortunate fellow human beings in other
countries. Clearly this is inconceivable.

It is indeed high time for plain speaking on this subject.
Many of those who are most vocal in demanding the immediate improvement of the lot of backward peoples would
be the first to oppose to the utmost any measure to end it if
it were to involve a substantial reduction in the standard of
living of the working classes in their own country. Indeed,
even the idea that, having regard to the increase in the
standard of living of working classes in advanced countries
since the war, the full benefits of further technological progress in, say, the next ten years should be used for raising the
standard of living of backward peoples, would be doomed to
rejection out of hand. To characterize the prevailing attitude,
let it be sufficient to recall that in 1955 Lancashire Members
of Parliament of both Parties were united in their demand
to ban the import of cotton textiles from India, Japan, and
Hong Kong to Great Britain and the British Colonies. They
adopted this line in spite of being aware of the obvious fact
that the exclusion of these imports would inflict hardship on
textile workers in underdeveloped countries, and would tend
to widen further the gap between their standard of living and
that of their Lancashire fellow-workers. Moreover this atti-

tude implies the demand that the East African peasants and laborers should be prevented from buying cheaper textiles from India, Japan and Hong Kong, and should be compelled to buy the much more expensive textiles of Lancashire. This would mean bolstering up and raising further the standard of living of Lancashire textile workers, at the expense of these East Africans, even though the Lancastrians are incomparably better off than those who are expected to make sacrifices for their benefit.

These facts are not pointed out in a spirit of hostile criticism of the attitude of the working classes in advanced countries, an attitude which is fully understandable. Attention is drawn to them in order to reinforce the argument in favor of speedy automation as the only means of bringing early relief to backward countries without calling for unacceptable sacrifices on the part of British, American, etc., workers. Since workers in advanced countries are, naturally enough, reluctant to give up their recently attained prosperity, the only solution of the problems of underdeveloped countries lies in a greatly increased productivity. Until recently an increase in output on a sufficiently substantial scale to enable advanced countries to assist underdeveloped countries effectively would have been considered inconceivable. Today, thanks to automation, it has come within the bounds of practical possibility. All that is called for is to allow automation to proceed unhindered, and to assist its progress to the utmost limits of our means, not only for the sake of further raising our own standard of living, but also for the sake of helping the peoples of backward countries.

Until recently there may have appeared to be some justification for arguing against large-scale assistance to underdeveloped countries, on the Malthusian principle—that any improvement above subsistence level tends to cancel itself out by bringing about an increase in the population. Beyond doubt, the problem of the high birth rate in many under-developed countries is a grave obstacle to an early substantial improvement in their living conditions. Nor is there much likelihood of a solution of the problem or even of its material mitigation by an increased practice of birth control. The only hope is that, thanks to automation, the increase in the population may be outpaced by an increase in production.

It is a favorite argument of those who believe in full-scale assistance to underdeveloped countries that, if only their standard of living could be raised above subsistence level, the birth rate would cease to increase after a while, and might even decline. They quote the example of western countries where the rising standard of living was in fact accompanied by a slowing-down of the increase in the popu-lation. Unfortunately this argument is not very convincing, because it overlooks social and religious factors which would operate against the popularization of birth control in many backward countries following on a rise in their standard of living. Even so, the idea that the maintenance of the standard of living above subsistence level for a few years would pro-duce the desired effect on the birth rate should not be rejected out of hand, because in it lies the only hope of the greater half of mankind to achieve a decent existence. The argument deserves to be given a chance to prove its worth. This could only be done if, with the aid of automation, the supply of goods in backward countries were to be raised to such an extent that it would outweigh any rising trend in their population. That rising trend is liable to continue for a few years, even if the rise in the standard of living were to produce eventually the effect attributed to it on the basis of western experience. To prevent its adverse effect on the stand-ard of living, the supply of goods would have to increase at a higher rate than that of the increase in population resulting from the higher standard of living through higher birth rate and lower death rate.

Those who, out of a narrow consideration for the immediate interests of a small section of the industrial workers in advanced countries, resist the progress of automation, incur a grave responsibility before history. In addition to handicapping progress in their own country, they prevent the only conceivable solution of the great problem of overpopulation and poverty in backward countries. While before the war such an attitude would have been guilty of selfishness only, today it has to be denounced also for its short-sightedness. In the meantime the attitude of the backward peoples toward their poverty has undergone a fundamental change. There is now evidence of a growing restlessness which is liable to culminate in explosion sooner or later. Anyone preventing a full development of automation in order to be able to give effective help to backward countries jeopardizes not only progress in his own country but the very existence of democratic civilization.

A substantial increase of unrequired exports from advanced countries to backward countries, in the form of both consumer goods and capital goods, is needed. The development of their own resources, with the aid of capital equipment supplied by the advanced countries, would enable the backward countries sooner or later to balance their international account. They could increase the production and export of materials, without which the expansion of output through automation in advanced countries would soon be checked by lack of materials.

Let us now see how far automation could contribute directly to the solution of the problems of underdeveloped countries, through its application within these countries themselves. According to some opinions, underdeveloped countries are at a great advantage compared with advanced countries, because there is no need for them to scrap obsolete plant in order to be able to proceed with automation. In an article appearing in the September, 1952, issue of *Scientific American,* Professor Leontieff goes so far as to say that industrially backward countries can solve their problem of industrialization by taking the dramatic short cut of building a few large automatic plants, instead of trying to progress by the slow and painful methods of the past. In other words, he expects backward countries to skip the phases of pre-automatic industrialization and, benefiting by the knowledge accumulated by the advanced countries, to catch up with them—indeed to cut ahead of them, unencumbered by costly plant, all of which the older industrial countries cannot afford to scrap immediately.

In reality, the balance of advantage is by no means on the side of backward countries. They are handicapped by scarce and costly capital but have plentiful and cheap labor. Labor-saving devices are not installed for the greater glory of technology. They are installed because there is not enough labor to produce the required output or because the cost of producing the goods by machine is lower than that of producing them by human effort. The first condition does not arise in most backward countries; they possess ample reserves of unskilled labor, consisting mostly of agricultural workers unable to earn a living on the land amidst conditions of overpopulation. For the same reason, unskilled labor is cheap. Its replacement by machine is less profitable than in advanced countries where unskilled labor is costly in addition to being scarce. The increase of productivity through automation must be much bigger in underdeveloped countries in order to make it worth while to replace man by machine.

From the point of view of the national economies of backward countries, it hardly pays to introduce automation so long as there are masses of unskilled labor trying to squeeze an inadequate living out of the land. Such labor is useless for automatic factories. On the other hand, the skilled labor that is required in large numbers is not readily available, nor can it be easily trained. If large numbers of skilled workers have to be imported, relatively little additional purchasing power is distributed among the poverty-stricken masses. The reason why industrialization tends to raise the standard of living in backward countries is precisely that it enables a large number of half-starved peasants to earn living wages in industry, and their earnings increase the national income. From this point of view automation leaves the problem of a better distribution of income in underdeveloped countries largely unsolved, at any rate until a sufficient number of their own nationals can be trained to replace imported skilled labor.

Lack of capital, either in the form of financial resources or in the form of capital-goods output, is an even more formidable obstacle to industrial automation in backward countries. They depend on foreign investment for the provision of most of the capital that would be needed for the automation of existing industries and for the creation of new automatic factories. It is to the interest of foreign countries to provide such capital for the purpose of increasing the output of food and raw materials, partly to prevent automation in the advanced countries being held up by shortages of raw materials. Foreign capital will probably be forthcoming for this purpose, especially as, with the progress of automation in advanced countries, the rising demand for raw materials would secure bigger profits on their production. For instance, growing demand explains the almost unlimited foreign capital that has been made available for oil production and refining in the Middle East.

Industries in underdeveloped countries which compete with established industries in advanced countries could greatly strengthen their competitive capacity by installing automatic factories. This, coupled with the low level of wages, would enable them to undersell their foreign rivals at home and even in foreign markets. But they would be heavily handicapped in more than one way. As Professor Arthur Lewis pointed out in his *Theory of Economic Growth,* the productivity of such new industries depends to a large degree on the pre-existence of other enterprise, especially of public utilities and engineering services. If they succeed in overcoming such difficulties as are liable to arise through lack or inadequacy of such enterprise, they will relieve the balance of payments of their countries by obviating the need for certain imports. But the problem of distribution of purchasing power would remain difficult to solve if the stage of non-automatic industrialization is skipped.

Beyond doubt, automation in backward countries would raise as many problems as it would solve. It seems, however, inevitable. Entrepreneurs cannot be expected to equip new works with obsolete machinery for the sake of giving employment to a larger number of their fellow-countrymen. Their profits will indirectly increase employment and income of the poorer classes. But real progress in that direction could be achieved more quickly and effectively by improving existing methods of agriculture, and by providing employment in largely non-automated mining. If foreign investors provide capital equipment for that purpose, they will largely contribute towards the raising of the standard of living of backward peoples and at the same time they will assist in the prevention of raw-material shortages in industrial countries.

CHAPTER TWENTY-ONE

THE IMPACT OF AUTOMATION ON NATIONAL DEFENSE

AUTOMATION made considerable progress during World War II. It reached its present stage largely through the stimulus given to its development by urgent and imperative requirements of national defense. Even now automation serves the needs of national defense to a very large degree. It serves them in various ways, some of which have a close bearing on the economic and social aspects of automation. The ways in which automation can assist national defense may be summarized as follows:

(1) Automation helps military research in its task of inventing weapons of attack and defense.

(2) It is actually applied in guided missiles, radar, etc.

(3) It can increase the efficiency of military administration in the same way in which it can help civil administration or the management of large businesses.

(4) It can assist staff planning of military operations by speeding up the elaboration of alternative plans.

(5) It greatly assists in the speedy production of the latest military equipment.

(6) It releases manpower from civilian occupations for the fighting services.

(7) It enables a community to increase production both for civil and military purposes.

From the point of view with which we are here concerned we only have to deal with the last three points. Thanks to the speed with which new equipment can be produced nowadays in automated factories, it has become possible to re-equip the fighting services with the latest devices without having to divert from civil production an unduly large part of industrial capacity. If the target is re-equipment within a given period of time, then, assuming that automation increases the speed of production four times, only a quarter of the capacity that would have been needed in pre-automation days has to be employed for the task.

It is often argued that, but for defense requirements, it would be possible to increase social-service benefits, to increase the production of capital equipment, and to raise the standard of living in general. But this argument ignores the fact that freedom from fear is, if anything, even more important than freedom from want. A defenseless and prosperous community offers the potential aggressor the maximum of temptation and the maximum of opportunity. Thanks to automation it will now be possible to raise the standard of living in spite of the continued maintenance of a deterrent to aggression in the form of adequate defense strength.

Automation enables the community to combine freedom from want with freedom from fear, because it enables industries with limited manpower to maintain and increase their output for civilian use, in spite of having to maintain and even increase their military output. Unfortunately automation provides the same assistance to the potential aggressor as to his potential victims. In fact, since the potential aggressors in our days are totalitarian dictatorships, they are well able to press ahead with automation for the purposes of rearmament, irrespective of the sacrifices inflicted thereby on the consumer. It is all the more important for democratic countries, not only for the sake of achieving a higher standard of living, but also for the sake of their national security in face of an ever-present threat of aggression, that they should proceed with automation with the utmost speed.

Admittedly economic and social temptation to disarm, or at any rate to neglect to maintain an adequate fighting force fully equipped with the latest weapons, is very strong. Many of those favoring disarmament by international agreement sincerely believe that a drastic cut in military expenditure would serve the cause of peace in addition to serving the cause of prosperity. But many others are unduly influenced, consciously or otherwise, by their overwhelming desire to raise the standard of living. To that end they would be prepared to run a certain amount of risk. They persuade themselves that the risk of concealed maintenance of armaments, or of secret rearmament by totalitarian states would be nonexistent, or at any rate negligible. Unfortunately, this is not a realistic view. It is doubtful whether adequate international inspection could ever be adopted to prevent the concealment of substantial quantities of weapons which are supposed to be destroyed under the disarmament agreement. Moreover automation has made speedy rearmament much easier for the aggressor. If Hitler had assumed power in 1953 instead of 1933, he would not have needed six years to prepare for war. Democratic countries would find it difficult to rearm on a large scale without being found out, but this would now be easier than ever for dictatorships. For this reason, safety from aggression lies in a more or less evenly balanced strength between the potential opponents, rather than in an advanced degree of disarmament based on some scrap of paper.

Thanks to automation, the maintenance of such strength need no longer be incompatible with an increase of prosperity. Admittedly it is always arguable that, but for the maintenance of adequate defense strength, automation would bring an even larger improvement in the standard of living. But such are the prospects of progress through automation that a reasonable degree of prosperity is no longer conditional on disarmament, any more than full employment is conditional on rearmament.

Industrial war potential is fully as important for national defense as the actual strength of the fighting services. For that reason, too, it is of vital importance for the democratic countries to proceed with automation with the utmost speed. This is being done in the Soviet Union, and the danger that the Communist bloc may catch us up in this sphere is very real. Given the immensely superior manpower of Communist countries, the only hope for the democracies to survive is to maintain the superiority of their industrial war potential. This end can only be achieved by proceeding with automation to the utmost limits of our capacity. The democratic countries can ill afford to slow down. This is one of the reasons why the development of inflationary conditions, which from time to time necessitate a temporary curtailment of production, and especially of capital investment, must be avoided. Those who, by excessive wage demands, contribute to the development of inflationary conditions, are guilty not only of sacrificing future prosperity for the sake of the satisfaction of their immediate requirements of unessential goods, but also of handicapping their country and the democracies in the maintenance of the superiority of their industrial war potential. Yet it is on that superiority that our survival as free nations depends.

Before World War II it was widely believed that an industrial country can only achieve full employment if it spends large amounts on armaments. This argument has been effectively disposed of by the experience of the postwar period. It is true that rearmament following the Korean War was an important factor in the postwar economy. But even before the outbreak of the Korean War full employment was largely achieved and maintained.

Yet the pre-war belief was not unfounded in relation to conditions of that time. Had automation developed before the war, it would have further accentuated unemployment and would have lent additional force to the argument that, under capitalism, rearmament is an essential condition of prosperity. Today civilian demand, stimulated by a flexible monetary policy and a more equal distribution of income, is capable of absorbing an unlimited industrial output. Any productive capacity that would become available for civilian purposes as a result of a disarmament, or of a limitation of armaments could easily be utilized in full for civilian purposes. Civilian demand would remain equal to any conceivable increase in the supply. Indeed the main difficulty is that, owing to the rapidly expanding consumer purchasing power, the high propensity to consume, and the expansion of the instalment credit system, demand is inclined to run ahead of supply.

Beyond doubt, the requirements of national defense slow down progress toward universal prosperity. In the absence of a major war, however, that progress is bound to continue, thanks to automation, in spite of the maintenance of considerable armed strength.

There is one aspect of the impact of automation on national defense which cannot be viewed without some uneasiness. It concerns the attitude of scientists and technologists towards the secrecy that necessarily surrounds their work in so far as it involves considerations of security.

Automation tends to increase the relative importance of

the scientist and the engineer in the community. Human nature being what it is, there is always a danger that any section of the community which gains such prominence develops an inclination to misuse its power. The danger is not that scientists and engineers will hold the community to ransom in the same way as laborers controlling vital services have done in recent years on many occasions for the purpose of securing higher pay. There is a totally different danger. Scientists and engineers may get it into their heads that, since they are so prominent in their respective spheres, they are qualified to lay down the law for the community. Many of them appear to imagine that since the politicians are incapable of ensuring the peaceful use of modern inventions, it is for the scientist to make good this omission. And by a chain of entirely unscientific emotional reasoning they arrived at the perverted conclusion that this end can be achieved by passing on information about the inventions to the potential enemies of their country. There is a good deal of loose talk about the need for an "international interchange" of scientific and technological secrets which are at present protected by security arrangements. Unfortunately this attitude has repeatedly been exploited in recent years for the benefit of communist-imperialist espionage. In practice the "international interchange" of technological secrets between the free world and the Communists has operated of course without any reciprocity on the part of the Communists. It simply amounted to delivering to them unilaterally the secrets on which the security and very existence of the free world may depend. There has never been any question of allowing the democratic countries to share the knowledge acquired in the laboratories and research stations of the Soviet Union. They are carefully guarded behind an impenetrable security curtain. But many scientists of the free world, brilliant as they are in their own line, are too naive to realize this obvious fact.

Many of these scientists were inspired by genuine idealism. The Communists took full advantage of this. They worked up a campaign of criticism against those scientists who "do not listen to the voice of their social conscience and allow their inventions to be withheld from mankind"—in other words, who comply with security regulations and refuse to betray their country to the potential enemy. The false arguments are put forward by crypto-Communists with the utmost skill, so that even many of those scientists who have remained loyal are assailed by doubts and by a vague feeling that they have failed in their duty to mankind. But in a number of known instances they allowed themselves to be persuaded into committing treason. Their credulity is liable to do incalculable harm to their countries and to the cause of democracy.

As often as not the naive idealism of these scientists is combined with a feeling of superiority. They fail to realize that, however first-rate they may be in their own respective sphere, they are dilettantes in the sphere of politics, and that they are children in the hands of those who play on their misguided idealism and on their vanity. Such men are dangerous. The progress of automation is bound to increase their prestige and power, and also their feeling of self-importance. From this point of view, automation is undoubtedly a dangerous development. One can only hope that, in the course of time, bitter but not fatal experience will make the new "ruling class" of scientists and technologists realize the true facts of the situation, before they allow themselves to be persuaded into causing their country and the free world some irreparable harm that would greatly outweigh the benefit derived from their scientific ideas and inventions.

In connection with the impact of automation on national defense, it is not without interest to try to assess the relative advantages and disadvantages of the Communist countries in the sphere of automation. For it seems probable that the outcome of the "cold war," and possibly even of a shooting war, will be largely determined by the relative extent to which the two opposing groups of countries are able to increase their economic war potentials with the aid of automation. Wishful thinkers in the western world were inclined until recently to assume the permanent inferiority of the Soviet bloc in the sphere of science and technology. It is becoming increasingly evident, however, that, in addition to the inventions secured from western countries through espionage, aided by the traitors among local Communists and fellow-travelers and by misguided scientists, Soviet Russia has made remarkable progress in recent years.

In view of the large number of scientists and technologists that are trained in Soviet Russia, the West can no longer take it for granted that it will be able to retain its lead in automation. And it would be idle to deny that, for the automation race, the Communist countries are in many respects at an advantage compared with the democratic countries. We might as well face the facts by listing these advantages, even at the risk that Communist propaganda might quote the list, carefully divorced from its context:

(1) Communist Governments are in a position to determine the pace of investment in automatic equipment by simply curtailing the production of consumer goods and diverting producing capacity towards the manufacturing of the required types of capital goods.

(2) They have full power to direct labor to where it is required to ensure a high rate of automation.

(3) There can be no question of resistance, either by individual workers, or by unions. The latter are merely the Soviet Government's meek and subservient executive organs, whose main task is to ensure that official plans and instructions concerning industrial production are carried out.

(4) Backward producing units can be forced to increase their rate of automation. In this connection the story quoted by Sir Walter Puckey, President of the Institution of Production Engineers, in his closing address of the Conference of the Institution in 1955 is characteristic, even if it is doubtful whether it could be authenticated. An official was sent from Moscow to find out why automation was not being adopted quickly enough on certain collective farms. He realized that there was opposition by people who had lived in those parts for a long time and he took certain steps to overcome it, with the result that shortly afterwards this telegram reached Moscow: "Have achieved first step in automation. Have shot all the horses."

(5) Owing to the standardization of production in Soviet Russia, without regard to the consumers' desire for wider choice, it is possible to produce manufactures in very long series.

(6) As consumer goods are permanently in short supply, it is possible to sell anything that is produced. Consumption has to adapt itself willy-nilly to the requirements of automation.

(7) The degree of inequality of taxed incomes is today much wider in socialist states than in some overtaxed capitalist states. For this reason inventive genius receives more financial encouragement in the Soviet bloc.

(8) There are no business cycles in Communist countries, and fear of a slump need not handicap the progress of automation. Nor do recessions interfere with the continuous flow

of demand or with capital expenditure on automation.

(9) Although there has been inflation in Soviet Russia and in other Communist countries since the war, it has been dealt with by compulsory price cuts, compulsory saving, and other measures which do not involve a curtailment of the volume of money available for financing automation.

(10) Balance-of-payments difficulties too are solved by means of direct control over production and foreign trade, and do not necessitate disinflationary monetary policies that would handicap automation.

Fortunately the Communist system has also some grave disadvantages from the point of view of the progress of automation. The following are some of them:

(1) Extensive government ownership and centralized control means a very high degree of red tape, inefficiency and corruption that is bound to handicap industrial progress in general and automation in particular.

(2) There is a very high degree of unintelligent political interference with the planning and execution of economic activities.

(3) Although the ever-present fear inspired by the ruthless methods of totalitarian dictatorship is an incentive to work harder, it discourages managements from taking initiative involving risk.

(4) Slave labor, which plays an important part in Soviet economy, is by its nature inefficient.

(5) Inventors are in many respects at a considerable disadvantage compared with their opposite numbers in the free countries. While the latter can submit their ideas to a large number of firms in addition to the government, in a Communist country the veto of a single individual or a single

authority kills an invention. This means that inventions are often doomed as a result of their rejection through errors of judgment, professional jealousy, personal antagonism, and other human failings—to which those upon whom the decisions rest are not immune in Russia any more than elsewhere. The difference is that Russian inventors are not given a second chance.

(6) Priorities in industrial production are established on a high level and are liable to be changed at any moment. Industries with a low priority are not allocated up-to-date equipment or first-rate labor.

It is impossible to form an opinion as to the side on which the balance of advantage lies, from the point of view of winning the automation race. But from the special point of view of defense with which we are concerned in this chapter, the Communist countries probably have the additional advantage of being able to use a higher proportion of automation for military purposes. The public is kept on short rations by the dictators of the Kremlin, and long-suffering consumers have no means even to criticize, let alone change, this state of affairs. The democratic peoples have no reason for envying the Soviet citizens for this "advantage" and for some other "advantages," the counterpart of which is represented by the curtailment of the Soviet citizens' freedom and human rights and the maintenance of a low standard of living. But realization that freedom and a high standard of living are handicaps in the automation race, especially from the point of view of national defense, is an additional reason for democratic countries to make a supreme effort to hold their own in that race, in spite of these handicaps.

CHAPTER TWENTY-TWO

ADVANTAGES OF AUTOMATION

ON THE basis of the examination of the various economic aspects of automation in the preceding chapters, we shall now attempt to sum up our findings and assess the advantages and disadvantages attached to its progress, in order to assist the reader in an attempt to arrive at a verdict whether, in the main, we stand to gain or lose by it. Doubtless, from the point of view of the engineer or the scientist, the progress of automation is well worth while even for its own sake. The immense possibilities opened up by recent inventions constitute a challenge to human inventive genius. But the attitude of the rest of us must depend on whether its progress contributes to human happiness.

In ultramaterialistic Soviet Russia the term "human happiness" is regarded as being synonymous with increase of output, even if an unduly large proportion of that increased output never reaches the consumer but assumes the form of war material or capital equipment aimed at increasing the economic war potential. But even in free countries, where the volume of consumer goods increases as a result of automation, such an increase would not necessarily add to human happiness if it were achieved at the cost of a deterioration of quality, or of a narrowing-down of consumer choice. Nor would it make for happiness if it were achieved through a deterioration of working conditions. If automation were to lower the dignity of human labor, it would be a matter of opinion whether the price paid for progress was not too high. It is a widely held opinion that the progress achieved by the Industrial Revolution was bought at a too high cost in terms of human happiness. The question is whether history is likely to repeat itself. There is much loose talk about a "Second Industrial Revolution" in connection with automation. Is automation likely to produce effects similar to those of the industrialization during the nineteenth century? If so there would indeed be a strong case against it. Fortunately conditions have since changed to such extent that there can be no danger of a repetition of history.

Before attempting to weigh the arguments against automation, let us summarize briefly the case for it. The following list of its advantages, in addition to recapitulating many points developed in earlier chapters, contains also some new points which could not be fitted into any of the chapters.

(1) Automation is bound to bring immense material gains to the community as a result of the increase in output. It opens up the vista of a hitherto undreamed-of expansion in production and consumption. This is the most obvious and most generally appreciated advantage of automation.

(2) Another obvious but considerably less unanimously popular result of automation is the mitigation of the scarcity of labor. From the point of view of unions this is listed among the disadvantages. From the point of view of the community, however, the labor-saving effect of automation represents undoubtedly a major advantage.

(3) Owing to the small size of the staffs required for

operating automated equipment, it is possible to organize work in two or three shifts. The machinery is used more intensively, and less of it has to be installed.

(4) Automatic factories require smaller buildings, and offices with electronic computers require less office space.

(5) Owing to the smaller number of employees required, there is no need for building the factories or offices in crowded urban areas, where labor is more easily available but land is expensive and the cost of living is high.

(6) Smaller staffs also mean less expenditure on devices of safety, hygiene, and various amenities.

(7) Owing to the small size of the shifts required, adequate reserve teams can be maintained at relatively moderate costs. This means that there is less likelihood of the work being held up for causes such as an influenza epidemic.

(8) The number of workers who are idle during slack seasons is small, so that it is not worth while to dismiss them. This means less seasonal unemployment.

(9) In many instances automatic equipment is actually cheaper per unit of output. This is particularly so if automation does not necessitate the scrapping of existing plant.

(10) Less working capital per unit of output is needed, because automation reduces the period of production. The value of goods in the pipeline at any given moment is smaller in relation to the output over a period.

(11) The time lost during work in process through delay between one process and another is reduced to a fraction.

(12) Transfer machines obviate the expense and delay involved in inventories that have to be taken between the various processes in non-automated factories.

(13) Automatic self-correction prevents wastage of materials pending the discovery and correction of faults. No time

need be wasted while samples are tested in laboratories. Testing is performed by the machine on the spot and is much more dependable.

(14) The continuous character of the process saves wear of machinery through frequent stopping and starting whenever the work piece is placed in position or removed.

(15) Automation secures a higher degree of uniformity and precision than human labor is capable of achieving. This is particularly important in the case of goods where very close tolerance is called for—for instance, turbine and compressor blades.

(16) Production is no longer limited by the limitations of human faculties and human skill. While human senses can only control one operation at a time, electronic devices can regulate simultaneously an involved system of interlocking controls.

(17) There is less risk to life, limb, and health in automatic factories, owing to the possibility of distant control and the elimination of the most difficult and dangerous tasks.

(18) Automation reduces fatigue considerably. Most of the physical exertions which had to be performed by human labor are now performed by machine in automated factories.

(19) Automation means more efficient management. Electronic devices supply more up-to-date information. Mistakes, changes in situations, etc., can be discovered more quickly. It takes less time to elaborate alternative plans.

(20) Office work of a routine character can be speeded up. As in factories, employees can be spared much drudgery and dull routine work.

(21) Automation tends to encourage standardization, because it is not usually worth while to incur its costs unless large quantities of identical goods can be produced. As a

result, former luxuries can be mass-produced at lower cost.

(22) Automation will bring more leisure in the long run. The increase in productive capacity can be used for a reduction of working hours instead of being used exclusively for increasing output.

(23) Automation raises the dignity of human labor. It tends to eliminate differences between office work and factory work. In the absence of the need for crowding many people within a limited space there is no need for irksome barrack regulations.

(24) Increased productivity opens up possibilities of wage increases unaccompanied by a degree of inflation that is liable to wipe out most of the gains.

(25) More intensified utilization of machinery enables managements to replace obsolescent equipment as soon as something better becomes available.

(26) Automation leads to specialization for the sake of mass-production. Big firms may prefer to confine their activity to the production of certain parts, leaving the production of other parts, or of semi-products, to specialist subcontractors.

(27) Automatic production of food is more hygienic. In flour mills, for instance, automatic conveying systems ensure a high degree of hygiene and keep the flour cooler, thereby reducing mildew and sweating.

(28) Automation facilitates scientific and technological research through the use of electronic computers.

(29) Increased productivity through automation greatly assists in the development of backward countries and in the raising of the standard of living of many hundreds of millions of people who are barely on a subsistence level.

(30) From the point of view of national defense, automation assists in the equipment of the fighting services with

modern weapons, without having to reduce production for civilian requirements.

The above list of advantages, though formidable, is far from exhaustive. It fully justifies the enthusiasm which automation inspires among scientists, engineers, businessmen and the general public. This favorable attitude is, however, far from unanimous, and even many of those who are in favor of automation are troubled by fears on account of its potential or actual disadvantages. So we propose to outline the other side of the picture in the next chapter. In this imperfect world of ours one seldom encounters unmixed blessings. The only question is whether or not substantial advantages of automation are liable to be outweighed by its disadvantages.

CHAPTER TWENTY-THREE

DISADVANTAGES OF AUTOMATION

MUCH of the various degrees of disapproval of automation in various quarters is due to sheer conservatism or to instinctive distrust inspired by any drastic change. The first railway, the first motor car, the first airplane aroused similar sentiments. The possibility of far-reaching economic and social changes resulting from automation is causing misgivings, especially among members of the older generation. This new development worries many of them, because they feel that "things are becoming too complicated," or that, as a result of automation, mankind will find itself even further removed from the natural state than it is at present. They grumble about life becoming increasingly artificial, and deplore the passing of the good old days of simple life. This attitude is almost as old as mankind itself. Conditions in the pre-automatic and pre-atomic age may well appear to us as very simple and unsophisticated, in spite of the fact that mechanization was already far advanced.

While mechanically-minded people welcome the latest triumphant achievement of engineering, those who are not built that way view the growing dependence of man on machine with gloomy forebodings. Indeed, some people even envisage the eventual replacement of man by robots. It is no wonder that some people show distinct signs of Erewhon complex in the form of fear of, and hostility toward, the latest automatic developments.

Apart altogether from such absurd sentiments, however, we encounter many practical and specific objections to automation. The following is a summary of the case against automation, together with the answers to it.

(1) Foremost among the objections is the one based on fears of large-scale unemployment. We saw in Chapter 7 that, although there is no likelihood of technological unemployment on a large scale, unemployment is liable to arise if we are left behind in the automation race.

(2) In particular there is much fear of a reduction in the demand for unskilled labor as a result of automation. But, since automation covers only a small part of industry, there is ample scope for unskilled labor in industries and other occupations unaffected by it. Moreover, the decline in the demand for unskilled labor is liable to be offset to a large extent by a gradual reduction of working hours. Taking a long view, there is no cause for objection to automation even from the point of view of those unskilled workers who cannot or do not want to acquire training.

(3) It is sometimes said that automation downgrades the laborer to the status of a servant to the machine. In fact the opposite is true. It must cause immense satisfaction to one's self-esteem to possess the power to set in motion and control a vast and highly involved engine. Workers have every reason to be thankful for being relieved of some of the tasks they had to perform before automation. It certainly puts an end to the nightmare which was so well brought out in Charlie Chaplin's film *Modern Times,* showing a worker at the assembly belt engaged in the deadly and monotonous task of tightening many thousands of bolts day after day throughout his life.

(4) In the last chapter we mentioned standardization

among the advantages of automation. It figures, however, also among the disadvantages. It is not beyond the capacity of human inventive genius, however, to devise automatic machinery which can be easily adjusted so that manufacturers are able to change their product. This is in fact already being done in some factories.

(5) It is feared that arts and crafts may get priced out of existence by reduced cost of manufactures resulting from automation. Even as it is, in many lines they barely hold their own, and if the price of manufactures can be reduced considerably the differentials in their respective prices might well become decisive. On the other hand a wider demand for craft-work and works of art is likely to arise, as a result of the rise in the standard of living, which will enable a larger proportion of consumers to indulge in their preference for handmade goods and in their desire to possess "something different."

(6) To comply with the requirements of automation, many manufactures may have to be redesigned in order to make them suitable for mechanical handling. Some at any rate may become less attractive. Any such tendency has, however, its natural limits because it is liable to encounter consumer resistance.

(7) The capital expenditure needed for the scrapping of existing plant and its replacement by the latest equipment is undoubtedly heavy. In many industries only the wealthy firms might be able to afford it. This is not necessarily so, however. New firms may find it actually cheaper to equip their factories with automatic machinery. There is a fair scope in many industries for the automation of small firms. In their specialized line, they may be quite competitive with much more powerful firms. Admittedly, in many industries automation is likely to bring about the absorption of smaller

firms by bigger units. There is, however, such a thing as an optimum size which limits the undue growth of units. Moreover there is a tendency, especially in the United States, for big firms to subcontract part of the work.

(8) Many firms in insecure and declining industries cannot afford to stage a recovery by adopting automation, which is a luxury reserved for the secure and prosperous industries. It is arguable that, as a result of automation, the declining industries may continue to decline while the prosperous ones expand further. But some declining industries at any rate could be given new lease of life through automation.

(9) The more complex the equipment of a factory is, the more vulnerable it is from the point of view of breakdowns, and the more far-reaching the effects of breakdowns are liable to be whenever they do occur. This disadvantage cannot be eliminated, but it can be mitigated by devising the machinery in such a way as to make it possible to replace easily the part which has become defective. A great deal can be done also by means of preventive maintenance, that is, the replacement of parts which have had a certain amount of wear before they are liable to become defective.

(10) A strike by a very small number of workers is liable to hold up an entire automated factory. This disadvantage is mitigated by the higher sense of social responsibility of educated middle-class workers employed in automated factories.

(11) Automatic equipment is liable to become obsolescent in a very short time. In our days inventions follow each other in a disconcertingly quick succession, especially in new lines such as electronics, or transfer machines, which are far from having reached maturity. Those on whom the responsibility for the decision rests are caught on the horns of a dilemma. They may feel that they cannot afford to risk committing themselves to investment in equipment that is liable to be-

come obsolete before it has paid for itself. On the other hand, neither can they afford to defer the automation of their plant pending the invention of something even better. In many instances such deferment is distinctly a case of the better being the enemy of the good.

(12) If the machinery is in constant use it leaves little time and opportunity for overhauling it. Under the continuous process the overhauling of any part of the machinery brings the entire process to a halt. In view of what we said in the previous paragraph, however, it is arguable that the accelerated wear of equipment is in a sense an advantage because it provides justification for an early replacement of obsolete equipment.

(13) There are bound to be various difficulties during the transition period while automation is adopted. Differences in labor conditions in automated and non-automated factories and, what is even worse, in various parts of the same factory in the course of transformation, are bound to give rise to much bitter feeling among employees, which requires careful handling. Many workers stand to lose through the changes, and they naturally resent the fact that other workers prosper at their expense. This is a social problem of considerable importance.

(14) From an economic point of view, automation has the disadvantage of making for unbalanced growth. Within the economy of a country, it is liable to upset the equilibrium as between various industries. Some of them will progress much faster than the others. Internationally the equilibrium is liable to be upset by the uneven progress of automation in various countries. The immense economic superiority of the United States is likely to increase further as a result of the high rate at which automation is progressing here, which will mean another period of worldwide scarcity of dollars.

(15) A much graver danger is the rapid progress of automation in the U.S.S.R. and some of her satellites. A vast increase in the output of manufactures by the Communist bloc, coupled with a sharp reduction in their cost of production in terms of man-hours, will create the possibility of a sweeping export drive, pursuing the end of political domination. Instead of exporting timber, coarse grain, oil, and other raw materials, which figured prominently among its exports during the early postwar period, the Communist group will be able to flood the world markets with textiles, engineering products, etc. This possibility is, however, an additional reason in favor of automation in democratic countries.

(16) There is a possibility of an exhaustion of irreplaceable raw materials through a too-rapid increase in the standard of living resulting from automation. Awkward bottlenecks are liable to develop. Planning on national and international scale is the only answer to this problem.

(17) Scarcity of vital materials is liable to cause friction between the "have" and the "have not" nations. It carries perturbing possibilities of conflicts.

(18) The above two points deserve attention also from the point of view of the danger to the stability of the markets of manufactures. Yet unless a steady market is assured, it may not appear worth while for many industries to embark on heavy capital expenditure which could only justify itself commercially through the maintenance of long runs of production.

(19) Business recession in a community that has achieved a high degree of automation is liable to be accentuated. However, it would be a very timid policy to oppose automation on the ground that a rising standard of living would increase the extent of a grave slump. Mankind cannot be expected to abstain from progressing for fear that the higher

it rises the bigger its possible fall is liable to be. Communities struggling around the subsistence level have little to fear. They have nothing to lose but their lives. With any progress the extent of a possible loss tends to increase. But this is no argument against progress. What matters is that automation itself does not increase the risk of a slump, even if it is liable to increase the gravity of a slump brought about by other causes. It is not progress of automation but lagging behind the automation race that would increase the risk of a slump.

(20) It has been suggested that automation increases the argument against *laissez faire* and in favor of planning, regimentation, totalitarian dictatorship. Many people fear that, unless the progress of automation is accompanied by controls, including direction of labor, it is liable to lead to crises. Experience in the United States has not so far borne out these fears.

(21) Automation is liable to accentuate a deflationary spiral through price reductions. Owing to the possibility of its uneven adoption as between firms in the same industry, the possibility of bankruptcies of the less auomatized firms must be envisaged. Wholesale bankruptcies are liable to cause an all-round depression. But in an inflationary climate, price cuts of an extent to produce such an effect are most unlikely.

Although the list of arguments against automation is undoubtedly formidable, there seems to be an answer to most of them. The sum total of the dangers and disadvantages may impress many people who only wish to see that side of the problem and who wish to make out a case against automation. But anyone who weighs impartially the list of advantages against the list of disadvantages is likely to feel that, in the main, automation is well worth having.

CHAPTER TWENTY-FOUR

WHAT IS THERE TO BE DONE?

Notwithstanding the disadvantages of automation examined in the last chapter, its immense advantages in the main are abundantly clear. Even those who are in favor of holding back its progress for fear of the dangers which, in their opinion, automation entails, must be aware of these advantages. In reality the dangers are not nearly so grave as the opponents of automation claim them to be. But it must be admitted that some of them are, in given circumstances, much more real than enthusiasts of automation would like to admit. The conclusion that emerges from our analysis is that, although there is little cause for concern as long as the economy continues to expand, automation is liable to exaggerate a slump or a depression if one should arise for no matter what reason. And woe unto him that is left behind in the automation race! He will suffer all the disadvantages of progress without enjoying its advantages. Two main conclusions follow from this. First of all, it is necessary to realize that the choice is not between risking the disadvantages of automation for the sake of its advantages or forgoing these advantages for the sake of being on the safe side. The choice lies between two sets of dangers. We may incur some unemployment in some given circumstances if we keep pace with the progress of automation, but we are likely to incur much more unemployment by lagging behind other countries. All military experts agree that casualties are usually much heavier during a retreat than during an advance. This being so, it is always advisable to try to advance rather than retreat, because apart from other reasons, a retreat does not save us from casualties.

The second conclusion is that the realization of the dangers inherent in automation should not induce us to reject automation, but should spur us to a supreme effort to reduce those dangers to a minimum. This book has contained many suggestions of ways in which the advantages of automation can be increased and its disadvantages reduced. The present chapter does not recapitulate all these suggestions but merely gives outlines of the most important policies and devices which, in our opinion, deserve consideration.

The development of automation has made it even more important than it was before to avoid slumps at all costs. So long as the national income continues to expand there is no real danger, provided that the progress of our automation keeps pace to a reasonable degree with that of rival industrial countries. But we must realize that we are riding the tiger and must on no account alight.

As we pointed out in our chapter dealing with business cycles, partial setbacks are liable to arise through the erroneous expansion of certain sections of industry, or from unexpected changes in demand, or from various other causes. There is, however, so much inflationary pressure in the situation that unemployment created by setbacks in individual industries can easily be absorbed by the rest of the economy. What we have to safeguard ourselves against is a general and substantial setback leading to a drastic curtailment of the national income. Owing to the overwhelming importance of this consideration, it may be advisable for those in charge of economic policy to err, if anything, on the side of inflation. Since it is almost impossible to keep the economy balanced all the time exactly halfway between inflation and deflation, there is, in existing circumstances, some justification for the official policy having a very slight inflationary bias. The ideal solution would be to avoid completely both inflation and deflation. But since from time to time this may become impossible, a very slight inflation may be the smaller evil.

On the other hand, substantial inflation carries with it the grave danger of a subsequent slump. Indeed, in conditions such as have existed since the war it is by far the gravest danger we have to guard ourselves against. Unless a country is prepared to put up with runaway inflation, or even with a too high degree of creeping inflation, a stage is bound to be reached at which its government feels impelled to take drastic disinflationary measures. These measures only aim at mopping up inflation, but if the degree of inflation they have to fight is high, the disinflationary action it calls for may have to be so drastic as to involve a certain risk of initiating a deflationary spiral.

It is therefore a matter of the greatest importance to check inflation before it reaches such a stage that the measures which have to be taken against it would have to be too drastic. Countries with a weak balance of payments are particularly vulnerable because they cannot afford much inflation without running into a balance-of-payments crisis. But even more fortunately placed countries, such as the United States, which have no balance-of-payment problems, could not afford to allow inflation to get out of control.

The best way of safeguarding ourselves against a slump is therefore to do our utmost to keep inflation within reasonable bounds if we cannot prevent it altogether. Even a well-conceived monetary policy executed with supreme technical skill is likely to be ineffective unless both sides of industry are willing to co-operate in an effort to avoid or keep down inflation. In face of a wage spiral the refined devices of scientific monetary management are helpless, unless they are applied in such overdoses as to break the wage spiral by creating unemployment. In that case they involve the risk of a slump. It is for the workers and their unions to exercise self-restraint to bring the wage spiral to a halt before it is too late. And it is for their employers to create the right atmosphere by keeping down their profits arising from automation. This can be done to some extent with the aid of reasonable price reductions. But, as we pointed out in Chapter 10, on the "Wages-Profits-Prices Triangle," there can be no ideal solution in respect of the sharing of the benefits of automation between employer, employee, and consumer.

There is no cut-and-dried formula on the basis of which all the disadvantages and risks can be avoided. Even if there were one, it would not be easy to persuade the interested parties to agree to its application. All that can be done is to try to strike a balance between the conflicting considerations, in order to avoid both inflation and deflation. This is easier said than done. But the realization of the risks involved in a mistaken distribution of the benefits of automation, through a careful study of the economic consequences of automation, should go some way toward creating a better atmosphere for understanding.

The workers should realize the need for a less uncompromising attitude toward profits during a period when it is necessary, in the interests of speedy automation, that the taking of risk on the part of entrepreneur and investor should be facilitated, encouraged and rewarded. On the other hand, excessive profits and dividend increases are liable to let loose an orgy of speculation, creating large unearned fortunes, stimulating luxury spending, encouraging wage claims, and generating class hatred. Here again it is necessary to strike a fair balance, but here again this is easier said than done.

Employers should be willing to relinquish a large proportion of the benefits of automation, by resorting to price reduction and, within reason, to wage increases. In totalitarian states price reductions can easily be ordered and enforced by the state authority. This was attempted even in some democratic countries on various occasions during the early postwar period. Business firms, appreciating the importance of avoiding inflation, should consent voluntarily to price cuts, or at any rate price freezes. If they fail to co-operate, governments may feel tempted to go beyond mere exhortation.

It is essential to maintain consumer purchasing power at a sufficiently high level to ensure adequate demand for the increased volume of goods. In conditions prevailing in the fifties there appeared to be no danger of inadequacy of consumer purchasing power. Nevertheless, it is important to bear in mind that the purchasing power of the masses must keep pace with expanding production, either through price cuts or through increased wages, to offset any deficiency in consumer purchasing power as soon as it appears. Above all, it is important to avoid declines of purchasing power through technological unemployment or large-scale downgrading of labor arising from automation, or through wholesale bankruptcies resulting from being left behind in the automation race. The purchasing power of the victims of progress must be maintained at a reasonable level.

In view of the operation of powerful influences making for inflation, the more immediate danger is not deficiency of purchasing power but excess of purchasing power. For this reason it is all-important to encourage saving. In the welfare-state atmosphere since World War II, working-class families with greatly increased earnings are inclined to spend to the limit of their incomes or even beyond it. The only economic justification for maintaining earnings at high levels would be more self-restraint on the part of their recipients. Otherwise, high earnings mean inflation, which again is liable to entail disinflationary measures, to the detriment of progress and stability.

Given the fact that the working classes are at present incapable of saving a sufficiently large proportion of increased earnings and that the prospects of an early and substantial increase in their propensity to save are not very good, it is of vital importance, in the interests of progress and stability, that they should abstain from excessive wage demands. In existing conditions it almost entirely depends on the unions whether or not automation will proceed at a satisfactory rate and whether its progress will bring prosperity or disaster. The main obstacle to rapid automation is the wage spiral, which is also the main potential cause of a slump in which automation would mean more unemployment. With each turn of the wage spiral the danger of a return to the bad old days is increasing. The industrial workers are masters of their own destinies. With a little self-restraint they can ensure for themselves a secure and prosperous future. Without it they expose themselves, for the sake of some immediate financial benefits, to the risk of large-scale unemployment, in addition to sacrificing the chances of the community to benefit fully by automation.

Perhaps the best solution of the wages-profits-prices triangle would lie in the wide adoption of the formula applied in the Guaranteed Annual Wage Agreement introduced in the American motor industry in 1955—to establish a trust fund for the purpose of paying increased unemployment benefits to workers who may have to be dismissed as a result of a setback in trade. Employers pay into that fund what they would otherwise have to pay in increased wages. This would moderate inflation during a boom and it would moderate deflation during a recession. In the chapter on fiscal policy we suggested tax concessions to workers on amounts they contribute to such "post-boom credits." The same principle should also be applied to excess profits earned through automation even though the bulk of it is needed for re-investment.

The advantages of automation could not be fully utilized if, from an excessive fear of technological unemployment, unions insisted on feather-bedding practices. It is to the interests of the community that workers who have become redundant in one industry should be made available for other tasks. The desire to mitigate hardships is understandable. Means should be devised, however, to encourage workers who have become redundant but who are retained owing to the strong bargaining power of their unions, to seek re-employment.

This is one of those situations in which the spirit of the interested parties matters much more than the elaboration of this or that ingenious formula. It is to the interests of the stability and prosperity, and even of the survival of the free countries that automation should proceed unhampered. If it is allowed to make good progress, the benefits derived from it by all sections of the community will be immense. If it is prevented from making progress, the losses that all sections of the community will suffer will be incalculable. Once these facts were realized there would be less inclination to grasp for the maximum of sectional benefit and more inclination to give and take in the interests of the common good. The advent of the Age of Automation accentuates the need for a higher degree of understanding and far-sightedness on the part of both employers and employees. The workers must overcome their hostility to profits in the interests of progress. Some degree of widening of income differentials is the price that those inspired by enlightened self-interest ought to be willing to pay. There is no sense in preferring equal misery to slightly less equal prosperity.

Industrial workers must realize that for them automation will bring not only a higher standard of living, more wages, more leisure and less fatiguing and health-destroying working conditions, but also greatly improved opportunities for upgrading. The best way to make them realize this is through a really impressive expansion of facilities for technological education. This is essential in order to meet the increased need of engineers of various kinds and of highly skilled workers capable of operating automatic equipment. But it is an equally important consideration that such a development would multiply the opportunities of members of the working classes for bettering themselves over and above the general improvement expected of automation.

The shifting onto technology of the main emphasis of the educational system in the free world must not be allowed to lead to the development of extreme materialism. In spite of the growing importance of technology for ensuring progress and security, spiritual values must not be neglected. It will be perhaps the most difficult of all the difficult problems arising from automation to ensure that mankind, in its impatient drive for material betterment, does not lose its soul.

However much we may admire the achievements of human inventive genius in the sphere of automation, we must not develop a quasi-religious worship of technology such as exists in Soviet Russia. And we must always remember that the goods and services, which the modern miracles of technology help to provide, are not ends in themselves, but only means to the supreme end of human happiness. A selfish scramble for an increased share in the expanding volume of material wealth can bring no happiness. It would be indeed a disaster for the human race if the splendid progress in technology witnessed in our lifetime were to generate nothing better than ruthless materialism, and if it were to accentuate class conflict instead of allaying it. Given sufficient patience and understanding for each other's point of view, our generation stands a good chance to live to see the day when there will be enough to satisfy to a reasonable degree everybody's needs, both material and cultural.

If, however, automation merely increases greed and selfishness, then mankind would have been better off if it had never been invented. Writing over fifty years ago Tolstoy said, "When the life of people is amoral and their relations are not based on love but on selfishness, then all technical improvement, the increase of man's power over nature . . . gives the impression of dangerous toys placed in the hands of children." In a class war over the proceeds of automation, as in a nuclear war, there can be no victors.

BIBLIOGRAPHY

(I) READINGS IN AUTOMATION

ADVISORY COUNCIL ON SCIENTIFIC POLICY: *Report on the Recruitment of Scientists and Engineers by the Engineering Industry.* (H.M. Stationery Office. London, 1955.)

BALDWIN, GEORGE B.: "Automation and the Skills of the Labour Force." *Improving the Work Skill of the Nation:* Proceedings of the Conference on Skilled Manpower, 1955. (National Manpower Council. New York, 1955.)

BRANTON, NOEL: "Economic Aspects of Automation." (*Accountancy.* December 1955.)

BRITISH INSTITUTE OF MANAGEMENT: Proceedings of the 1955 National Conference. (Reprinted in *The Manager.* December 1955.)

BROWN, GORDON S., and CAMPBELL: "Controls Systems." (*Scientific American.* September 1952.)

BUCKINGHAM, WALTER S.: "Industrial Implications of Automation." (*Monthly Labour Review.* May 1955.)

CALHOUN, ROBERT L.: "Paper on Personal Morale Today." (Eugene Staley ed. *Creating an Industrial Civilization:* A Report on the Corning Conference. Harper. New York, 1952.)

CHIEF INSPECTOR OF FACTORIES: Annual Report for 1954. (H.M. Stationery Office. London, 1955.)

CHAMBER OF COMMERCE: "Automation." (*Economic Intelligence.* Washington, November 1955.)

COUNCIL FOR TECHNOLOGICAL ADVANCEMENT: *Automation and Job Trends.* (Chicago, 1955.)

DIEBOLD, JOHN: *Automation: The Advent of the Automatic Factory.* (Van Nostrand. New York, 1952.)

248

"Automation: The New Technology." (*Harvard Business Review*. December 1953.)

"The Impact of Automation on Human Relations." (59th Conference of American Industry. December 1954.)

DRUCKER, PETER F.: "The Promise of Automation." (*Harper's Magazine*. April 1955.)

ENGLAND, WILBUR: "Automatic Merchandising." (*Harvard Business Review*. December 1953.)

ENGSTROM, ELMER: "Automation." (Address at the Centennial Symposium on Modern Engineering, University of Pennsylvania, Philadelphia, Pa. December 1955.)

FAIRLESS, BENJAMIN F.: *Our One Indispensable Weapon*. (United States Steel Corporation. New York, 1955.)

GARDINER, MARTIN: "Logic Machines." (*Scientific American*. March 1952.)

INSTITUTION OF PRODUCTION ENGINEERS: *The Automatic Factory: What does it Mean?* (Report of the Conference held at Margate. June 1955.)

JOINT COMMITTEE ON THE ECONOMIC REPORT, CONGRESS OF THE UNITED STATES: *Automation and Technological Change*: Report of the Subcommittee on Stabilization, and Hearings before the Subcommittee. (U.S. Government Printing Office. Washington, 1955.)

LEONTIEF, WASSILY: "Machines and Man." (*Scientific American*. September 1952.)

LOCKSPEISER, SIR BEN: "Man and his Machine." (Address delivered to the British Association, Bristol, September 1955. Reprinted in *British Management Review*. October 1955.)

NAGEL, ERNEST: "Automatic Control." (*Scientific American*. September 1952.)

NATIONAL ASSOCIATIONS OF MANUFACTURERS: "Automation and Jobs." (*Industry's View*. December 1955.)

P.E.P. (POLITICAL AND ECONOMIC PLANNING): "Towards the Automatic Factory." (*Planning*. June 1955.)

SLUCKIN, W.: *Minds and Machines*. (Pelican Books. London, 1954.)

WADDELL, H. L.: "Progress in Automatic Production." (Annual Meeting American Society of Mechanical Engineers, 1952.)

WIENER, NORBERT: *The Human Use of Human Beings.* (Second Edition, Revised. Doubleday, New York, 1954.)

(2) ECONOMIC BACKGROUND

ABRAMOVITZ, MOSES: *Inventories and Business Cycles.* (Princeton, Princeton Univ. Press, 1954.)

AKERMAN, JOHAN: *Economic Progress and Economic Crises.* (London, 1932.)

BROWN, A. J. YOUNGSON: *The American Economy.* (New York, Library Publishers, 1951.)

COX, REAVIS: *The Economics of Instalment Buying.* (New York, Ronald, 1948.)

DUESENBERRY, JAMES S.: *Income, Saving, and the Theory of Consumer Behavior.* (Cambridge, Harvard Univ. Press, 1949.)

EINZIG, PAUL: *Inflation.* (New York, Macmillan, 1952.)
How Money Is Managed. (England, Penguin, 1954.)
"The Dynamics of Hire-Purchase Credit." (*Economic Journal.* March, 1956.)

FELLNER, WILLIAM: *Monetary Policies and Full Employment.* (Berkeley, Univ. of California Press, 1947.)

FLORENCE, P. SARGANT: *The Logic of British and American Industry.* (Chapel Hill, Univ. of North Carolina Press, 1953.)

GALBRAITH, JOHN KENNETH: *The Great Crash. 1929.* (Boston. Houghton Mifflin, 1955.)

HALD, EARL C.: *Business Cycles.* (Boston, Houghton Mifflin, 1954.)

HAMBERG, D.: *Business Cycles.* (New York, Macmillan, 1951.)
Economic Growth and Instability. (New York, Norton, 1956.)

HANSEN, ALVIN H.: *Business Cycles and National Income.* (New York, Norton, 1951.)

HANSEN, ALVIN H., and CLEMENCE, RICHARD V.: *Readings in Business Cycles and National Income.* (New York, Norton, 1953.)

HARROD, R. F.: *The Life of John Maynard Keynes.* (New York, Harcourt, Brace, 1952.)

HAWTREY, R. G.: *Cross Purposes in Wage Policy.* (New York, Longmans, Green, 1955.)

HAYEK, FRIEDRICH A.: *Monetary Theory and the Trade Cycle.* (London, 1933)

HEGELAND, HUGO: *The Multiplier Theory.* (Lund, 1954.)

HICKS, J. R.: *A Contribution to the Theory of the Trade Cycle.* (Oxford, 1950.)
"Economic Foundations of Wage Policy." (*Economic Journal*, September 1955.)

HUTTON, GRAHAM: *We Too Can Prosper.* (New York, Macmillan, 1953.)

KEYNES, JOHN MAYNARD: *A Treatise on Money.* (New York, Harcourt, Brace; 1930.)
The General Theory of Employment, Interest and Money. (New York, Harcourt, Brace; 1936.)

KURIHARA, KENNETH K. (ed.) : *Post-Keynesian Economics.* (New Brunswick, Rutgers Univ. Press, 1954.)

KUZNETS, SIMON: *Economic Change.* (New York, Norton, 1953.)

LEWIS, W. ARTHUR: *The Theory of Economic Growth.* (Homewood, Irwin, 1955.)

LUNDBERG, ERIK: *Studies in the Theory of Economic Expansion.* (Baltimore, Johns Hopkins, 1955.)

LUNDBERG, ERIK (ed.): *The Business Cycle in the Post-War World.* (Proceeding of a conference held by the International Economic Association.) (In press, New York, St. Martins.)

MILLIKAN, MAX F. (ed.): Income Stabilization for a Developing Democracy. (New Haven, Yale Univ. Press, 1953.)

OHLIN, BERTIL: The Problem of Employment Stabilization. (New York, Columbia Univ. Press, 1955.)

ROBERTSON, SIR DENNIS: *Utility and All That, and Other Essays.* (New York, Macmillan, 1952.)

ROBINSON, JOAN: *An Essay on Marxian Economics.* (New York, St. Martins, 1947.)

ROSTOW, W. W.: *The Process of Economic Growth.* (New York, Norton, 1952.)

SCHUMPETER, JOSEPH A. (Transl. by Redvers Opie): *The Theory of Economic Development.* (Cambridge, Harvard Univ. Press, 1934.)

SCHWARZ, SOLOMON M.: *Labor in the Soviet Union.* (New York, Praeger, 1953.)

SMITHIES, ARTHUR, and BUTTERS, J. KEITH (eds.): *Readings in Fiscal Policy.* (Homewood, Irwin, 1955.)

STALEY, EUGENE: *The Future of Undeveloped Countries.* (New York, Harper, 1954.)

TINBERGEN, JAN, and POLAK, J. J.: *The Dynamics of Business Cycles.* (Chicago, Univ. of Chicago Press, 1950.)

TURVEY, RALPH (ed.): *Wages Policy under Full Employment.* (New York, Macmillan, 1952.)

WHITTLESEY, CHARLES R.: *Principles and Practices of Money and Banking.* (Revised, New York, Macmillan, 1954.)
Readings in Money and Banking (New York, Norton, 1952.)

WRIGHT, DAVID McCORD: *The Economics of Disturbance.* (New York, Macmillan, 1947.)

INDEX

Date Due